A brief 'I spy' guide to places associated with the fishing industry past and present in Devon; and a contemporary photographic record of the registered fishing boats kept in these places.

The Fishing Boats & Ports of Devon

An Alternative Way to Explore Devon

by
W. Stewart Lenton
(With additional research and introduction by Liz Lenton)

Channel View Publishing Plymouth
Channel View, Andurn Estate, Down Thomas
PLYMOUTH PL9 0AT

Published in 2006
By Channel View Publishing Plymouth
Channel View, Andurn Estate, Down Thomas,
Plymouth PL9 0AT
slenton@btinternet.com
www.fishportboats..co.uk

ISBN
0-9554023-1-X 978-0-9554023-1-9

Photographs on the Front Cover:-
Above - Fishing boats in Clovelly Harbour
Below - Fishing boats at Sidmouth
Photographs on the Back Cover:-
Left to right and top to bottom
Fishing boats in Brixham Harbour, PH322 'Metan' & PW32 'Cornish Gem' at Plymouth
PH271 'Kelly J' & HL 125 'Boy Scott', Fresh Fish for sale in Beer, Boat decoration at Brixham on BM488 'Thankful'
Ex E289 'Pearl' on Beer Beach
Brixham Trawler 'Provident', Clovelly Harbour, Torquay Harbour,
Seaton, Roadside Wild flowers, BM24 'Peace & Plenty III' at Brixham.

This book is dedicated to my wife whose help and enthusiasm in writing and compiling this book has added to the enjoyment of the task.

Acknowledgements

We are indebted to ;-

Newlyn Fish Cellar and Museum (closed October 2005) for permission to take the photographs which appear on page xxvii

Fisheries Research Services for permission to use Crown copyright diagrams from Fisheries Research Service Scottish Fisheries information pamphlet No 25 2004 *'An introduction to commercial fishing gear and methods used in Scotland.' (RD Galbraith & A Rice after ES Strange)* These appear as figures 3, 4 & 8 on pages xxi & xxvi of this book respectively.

David Linkie, Editor of 'Fishing News' & 'Fishing Vessels of Britain & Ireland', for a few photographs marked (DL).

To Michael Veale for his kindly interest, painstaking and laborious reading of the proofs with helpful suggestions ; and to many other friends and acquaintances, including George Hogg & Alison Hodge whose encouragement and suggestions have influenced the way this book has evolved.

Every effort has been made to get the information and details of boats correct at the time of writing. However boats are continually moving around and sometimes spend different times of year in different ports which might account for some discrepancies. Much information has been obtained by detective work . If any errors are spotted I apologise, and would be very grateful for any information to correct it for future versions of the book. Please contact me via e-mail at slenton@btinternet.com or through

Channel View Publishing Plymouth
Channel View
Andurn Estate, Down Thomas
Plymouth , PL9 0AT

FORWARD
by George Hogg, Hon Archivist of the National Maritime Museum, Falmouth

The Fishing Boats and Ports of both Devon & Cornwall started off in a very different way from most books. The original idea was to produce an easy identification guide to the fishing vessels which Stewart and his fellow watchkeepers at the National Coast Watch Institution saw passing their lookout station at Rame Head. Stewart noticed that when skippers called up on the radio to identify their boats they invariably gave only the names of their vessels, which are not easy to check, especially when the sea is rough, so Stewart made up a display book of photos that he took of the local vessels. This proved so successful that he produced other displays for the volunteers manning the lookouts in other parts of both Devon and Cornwall.

Stewart and his wife travelled many hundreds of miles to visit all the fishing ports in Devon and Cornwall to photograph all the fishing craft in the region. These trips led his wife Liz to write the general introduction to the ports which appears at the beginning of the book. This section will be a very great help to many visitors as it will enable them to see beyond the gulls and brightly coloured boats which fill our ports. An excellent section on fishing methods follows which will enable readers to understand how boats are rigged to catch different types of fish.

All readers will find much to interest them in the main body of these books which contain some 1450 up to date photographs of the region's fishing craft carefully arranged in the order of the ports from which they fish. These photographs are not only an "I Spy" guide, but when taken as a whole, provide the historian with an unique overview of the fishing activity in Devon and Cornwall in 2006. The inclusion of dates on all the photographs is vital as individual boats often change their ports and appearance. The comprehensive index at the end of the books provides a very valuable check list for all the users of these books.

I have no doubt that this book which has been produced as the result of one man's idea to produce a recognition aid for the watchkeepers at Rame Head will be read and enjoyed by many people from all walks of life. I am most grateful to Stewart for writing it and providing me, as a historian, with an unique and most valuable insight into the fishing activity in the region.

11 September 2006.

NOTES ON HOW TO USE THIS BOOK

PORTS

After the introduction **details of the Devon ports follow in clockwise order round the coast**, starting with Clovelly on the North Devon Coast round to Lynmouth, and then going south to Seaton on the South Devon Coast and back to Plymouth and the Cornish border on the South coast.

Each Port is identified on the map inside the front cover by a number in Blue which also appears on the left hand side of the coloured title bar for the corresponding Port description. *It will be noticed that Clovelly although the first Devon port to be considered is number 44. This is because the Cornish ports (in red numbers on the map) start with the River Tamar at 1 and end with 42 The Isles of Scilly. The Cornish Ports from 1- 42 are considered in the sister book 'The Fishing Boats & Ports of Cornwall'*

The Contents index on page vi gives the page number where each port section begins.

On the section for each Port there are;-

a. **Some brief details about the port**, and where applicable, notes on other landing places in the area, and photographs of the Port.

b. **A list of boats** seen to be operating from that port since 2003 in alpha-numerical order of registration (see below)

c. **Photographs of each boat** in the same numerical order as the list of boats in that port.
Below each photograph is the date on which it was taken and the name of the boat.

BOATS

The list of boats (b. above) operating from each port indicates -

Type of fishing, Length overall in metres, Engine Kilowatt power, Year and country of manufacture.
In the column for hull construction,

S=Steel, W=Wood, and F=Fibreglass

A 'p' against the boat's name indicates that there is a photograph of that boat.
No 'p' means that a photograph has not been taken (either because the boat has moved from the area, or just not been seen!)

At the end of the book is included:

Two lists of all the boats known to be operating from Devon and Cornwall including the Isles of Scilly

The first list is in alpha-numerical order of registration. Included in this list are all the port registrations around the UK coasts many of which feature on the boats in Devon. In this list most of the known boats of the local area registrations have been included for completeness, even if they are no longer operating. (Note that in Devon eg on the River Exe and at Bideford there are locally registered boats bearing the registration letter 'E' (for Exeter) and 'B' for Bideford which are similar to the national registration identification numbers

The second list is an alphabetical list by name of all the Devon & Cornwall boats.

To find the photograph of a particular boat

1. Look up either the name in the alphabetical list, or the number in the alpha-numeric al list.
2. Note the home port of the boat,
3. Then consult the relevant port pages *(for page number see contents index on page v)* and look up the boat in the photographs of boats in that port which are in order of registration number.(See c. above) .

No list will ever be completely up to date since there is a continual state of change, as boats get bought and sold, new vessels arrive on the scene, and older vessels are either de-registered, scrapped or left to die gracefully. Boats can also change appearance as they get repainted in different colour schemes, or even undergo more dramatic modifications, such as a change in position of the wheelhouse as illustrated by the photographs in the introduction - pages xiv to xviii

Boat Spotting - It is suggested that as you visit the ports and coast and personally find each boat, you can indicate this by ticking the 'p' column in pencil, or keeping a separate list of boats seen with the date they were seen inside the back cover. *(This may be continued on separate sheets tucked into the book as required.)*

Contents

Introduction .... page vii

Examples of Changes in Appearance of Fishing Vessels xiv
Types of Fishing Vessels xx
Administrative & Registration Centres xxix

SECTION 2 - PORT PAGES (North Devon)

43 **Clovelly** .... Page 1
44 **Appledore** 3
45 **Bideford** 5
46 **Barnstaple** 7
47 **Ilfracombe** 8
48 **Lynmouth** 10

SECTION 3 - PORT PAGES (South Devon)

49 **Seaton** 12
50 **Beer** 15
51 **Branscombe Mouth** 18
52 **Sidmouth** 19
53 **Budleigh Salterton** 20
54 **Exmouth** 22
55 **Teignmouth** 29
56 **Torquay** 34
57 **Paignton** 37
58 **Brixham** 39
59 **Dartmouth** 58
60 **Torcross** 64
61 **Beesands** 65
62 **Salcombe** 67
63 **Hope Cove & Bigbury on Sea** 74
64 **River Yealm** 75
65 **Plymouth** 77

Section 4 Some Visiting Fishing Vessels to the South West page 96

Index Alphabetical
Index Alphanumerical

INTRODUCTION

This book and its sister book 'The Fishing Boats and Ports of Cornwall' is intended to be more than just a colourful collection of fishing boat photographs although it started out as an identification aid of fishing boats. We hope that it will be used be as an incentive to find the boats and places illustrated here, perhaps as a family or group activity. This should give the reader a more interactive experience in exploring the coastal area and encourage them to build up knowledge about our fishing and coastal heritage, rather than just admiring the fishing boats as the colourful and picturesque addition to the wonderful scenery of the Devon coast that they undoubtedly are. This introduction is written by the photographer's wife to illustrate how somebody starting with absolutely no interest in fishing boats could develop a passion for this pursuit, awakening interest in the fascinating history behind the fishing industry and things that have been allied to it over the centuries. We were relative newcomers to the area when we started collecting fishing boat photographs as an identification aid for the National Coastwatch Station at Rame head where my husband is one of the volunteer watch keepers. We had great fun exploring the coastal areas and looking for fishing boats, and also gathering snippets of information which we share with you here in the hope that this might stimulate an appetite to find more for yourself.

Colourful fishing boats in Brixham

Looking for places where fishing boats might be found has taken us, not only to well known fishing ports, but also to out of the way, rugged and picturesque tiny coves, and sheltered harbours, where a few small boats can still be found, feeding our imagination about what might have been in generations past. Apart from the relative lack of fishing activity now, such places, in their natural beauty, particularly when seen outside the tourist season, could hardly have changed since they were the centre of thriving little fishing communities of our grandparent's or great grandparent's time. Because it can never be guaranteed in any one visit to a given location that all the fishing boats will be seen, several trips may be necessary to spot all the boats listed there. Other boats may be found that were not there when these photographs were taken, in which case your sense of achievement will surely be as great as ours when we ventured forth yet again to a particular place and unexpectedly found that we could add another boat to our collection.

As one begins to penetrate the close knit fishing community one catches a tantalising glimpse of a wealth of tradition and customs that evoke nostalgia for bygone times. It is in such communities that we have a bridge with the past, because here so much that we have lost in our present day world still remains. The admirable traditions of courage in adversity, looking after ones own, the respect for elders, and wisdom passed down from father to son, and mother to daughter, keep alive for us so much that is precious in our own island heritage. Fisher folk, although friendly and generous,

Fishing boat 'Bethany' adding colour to the beach at Beer

are however jealous of their life style, and can be suspicious of outsiders who come to question, particularly with the changes and regulations being imposed from various authorities concerned with conservation issues and the like, at the beginning of this twenty first century. These changes may themselves make a photographic collection such as this of historical interest in years to come.

Already affected by changes in fish stocks caused by global warming, over fishing, various conservation issues, quotas and rising fuel costs, some boats have been laid up as owners have found it more difficult to make a living, or less worthwhile to take the considerable risks of putting to sea following the trade of their forefathers. When a more comfortable activity can be found to support their families, the temptations to forsake the old occupation must be great. It is said that on average in the UK 114 fishermen are killed or seriously injured and 28 fishing vessels are lost each year and 370 accidents are reported. Fishing is said to be the most dangerous job in the world! There are risks every day with working in a wet, icy, slippery and moving environment. Rough seas can take a man overboard and deployed fishing gear would make it impossible to turn the boat in time to save him from perishing in freezing cold waters. There can be risks in being in a confined space near working equipment. For example the thick wire ropes attached to nets can be winched in under considerable tension because of a heavy catch which may include rocks as well as fish. This tension can be dangerously increased if nets should snag on something on the sea bed. Crewmen risk serious injury or death should the wire ropes snap. All are facts to make you appreciate the fish on your plate or question if you should eat fish at all! Skippers must constantly balance the cost of fuel used up travelling to distant fishing grounds for only a possible improvement in catch. The general running costs of the boat could well outweigh the price obtained for the catch at market, and there would then be difficulty in paying the crew a living wage. Selecting where to fish and the kind of fish that would be caught in a given region is not an exact science. Much depends on instinct and the previous experience of the skipper. Damaged nets are always a risk. It might be necessary to cut adrift nets which become snagged on objects on the sea bed compromising the safety of the boat itself, and if retrieved they require additional time to effect repairs when there can be no fishing. The number of days at sea are regulated so must not be wasted. Sacrificed nets on large trawlers could cost over £30,000 to replace but the cost to the environment is not so easy to calculate. 'Orphaned nets' of modern non degradable materials can continue passive fishing over many years without quotas, and can trap endangered species and cause damage to other boats. Boats at sea need to land sizeable catches each day - but not of the wrong fish. If they are licensed for example to fish for prawns, and they catch fish instead - only a limited number of these can be marketed - any surplus must be returned to the sea even if they are already dead!

1 Pony Power

Smart Crossing Dartmoor

Wild flowers by roadside

Not so wild but colourful!

In looking for fishing boats and ports you will not only discover fishing boats of all shapes, sizes and colours, but a wealth of wild flowers, and the wonderful vivid and contrasting colours of sea, shore, and surrounding countryside, depending on the season in which you visit. Colourful plastic boxes, (which are a different colour for each port) packed with ice are used to contain the fish adding further colour to the quayside.

Generally speaking, the best time to explore is outside the high tourist season, especially for ease of travelling down narrow lanes, and for enjoyment of the solitude at your destinations. We have found our SMART car invaluable for negotiating narrow lanes and making use of parking spots too small for others – although somewhat hard in the suspension if you encounter many bumps in the road! Once at your destination, either simply drink in the peacefulness, perhaps as a refreshing experience away from daily life, or let the imagination travel to times long past of smugglers, wreckers, and all who lived and loved to be beside the sea. We found that the wife did more of this sort of thing, often from the shelter of the car, particularly on days when the weather was less conducive to walking, while the photographer went in search of the boats alone. During suitable weather it is often easy and rewarding to combine the search for fishing boats and fishing ports with walking parts of the nearby South West Coast Path because this path not only provided a means for local coastal communities to connect together but it was actually developed for the Coastguard and Excise officials to be able to patrol the coast for smugglers. In order that they could do this efficiently they had to have extensive views out to sea and also into coves, inlets and harbours - the very places where our fishing boat quest needs to take us.

Historic Clovelly Harbour on the North Devon Coast With its Ancient Stone Breakwater

Places like Beer, Hope Cove, and Burgh Island and Clovelly are associated with smuggling. For those on the Southern Coast it is only a few hours sailing from the contraband goods like brandy, wine, tobacco, tea, and luxury goods, to be obtained in France, but places on the Northern coastline although further from the continent provided less chance of being caught as the Excise Men concentrated on the south. An interesting legend developed about the existence of cannibals around Clovelly. It is said that the Smugglers put out the story that human remains were preserved in casks hidden by cannibals inside certain caves in the hope that people would be deterred from going into these places where they had in fact hidden their contraband goods. The less hospitable northern coastline of Devon & Cornwall is also often associated with the 'Wreckers'. They would not only take advantage of plundering the ships which came to grief in fierce seas on the rugged coastline, but they might actually deliberately lure ships to their fate on the rocks with the use of 'false lights', an offence which was made punishable by death in the eighteenth century.

Smuggling was much linked with the Pilchard Industry of the past, not only because the boats and their moorings easily adapted to this, but it was particularly tempting if the pilchards did not come, or shoals and catches were small. It prevented boats from being left idle, and helped finance such periods when the fisherman themselves would be unemployed — long before the advent of a welfare state. It also became almost a commercial necessity because pilchard processing required so much salt, which was a taxed commodity. It is said that officials were often inclined to be lenient in the enforcement of anti-smuggling measures concerning salt, and some were even engaged themselves in such smuggling.

In exploring the coastal areas of Devon you may find signs from the A379/A381 to an attractive little place called Hope Cove situated between Thurlestone and Salcombe. The Cove was extensively used by fisherman in the 18th century when many small boats were launched from the beach, as well as larger boats moored in the bay itself. This is a quintessential Devon Fishing Village (actually two villages - Outer and Inner Hope)

Hope Cove

complete with thatched cottages and shingle and sand beaches where lobster pots and small boats can be seen. These days it does not have any registered fishing boats of its own. The registered boats are all now in Salcombe, but locals still supplement their income with small time crabbing and lobster pots for which they now use unregistered boats. These are not regulated but not expected to fish on a commercial scale. Having said that, a de-registered boat originally from the port of Plymouth, recently had the double misfortune to have been broken up on rocks near Ilfracombe and, it is said, to have been found with a catch on board sufficient in quantity very much for commercial purposes! Until the Pilchards mysteriously stopped arriving off the South West coast in large shoals in the 1930's Hope Cove was known as 'Pilchard Cove'. In the 1750's, it is said that one fishing boat not far from the shore, in one draught took around 20,000 Mackerel.

Sea fog surrounding Burgh Island as seen from Bigbury - Hotel just visible

Many wrecks have occurred at the coast near the village over the years and in 1936 the 334 foot, four masted vessel 'Herzogin Cecilie' ran aground on the Ham Stone just off shore. A visit to Hope Cove has its own rewards in the old world architectural charm, good walks, and a variety of places where a drink, a Devon tea, or something more substantial can be enjoyed. Your imagination will tell you that such a place had to be an old time smugglers haunt! If you need more food for the imagination you might consider the legend of the beautiful woman who owned a cabin in Outer Cove and who would entertain Excise Men in the 'Bird in Hand' Inn keeping their mind off their work whilst smugglers escaped through a trap door in the floor of her cabin to a passage below and out to sea. The remains of this passage nearest to the sea is stilll there in the form of a large cave which is exposed at low tide and apparently extends back 25 yards through a fault in the rock which is thought to have communicated with the smuggler's escape passage. The smugglers would obtain their booty of luxury goods from France including kegs of finest cognac by rendezvousing off the coast with three masted luggers. The kegs would be temporarily suspended along the outside of their boats below the water line, and carried to areas where they could be stored on the sea bed, or in the sea, for retrieval when it was safe to bring them ashore under cover of darkness. The fisherman had their own names to identify specific areas of sea where they had found good fishing, or they had hidden contraband, and they could identify these by taking bearings on various combinations of land features.

Egret in Avon Estuary

Wader in Avon Estuary

Not far from Hope Cove you may visit Burgh Island off Bigbury – now long since taken over by the seaborne leisure industry, or devotees of Agatha Christie and Art Deco, on visits to the island hotel. Here you can find some evidence of the pilchard fishing industry in the form of what some say was probably a ruined Huer's hut at the crest of the island's hill for the nearby fishing beach of Challaborough, and the 14th century 'Pilchard Inn' pub, a former fishing cottage which for some time was the hideout of Tom Crocker the well known Smuggler. Tom Crocker was in fact shot and killed outside this building by an Excise man who managed to catch up with him. See if you can find a memorial to him and his executioner. (Slake your thirst at the same time!) If you have a good sense of imagination, you may even 'hear' the distant sound of the Huer shouting through his long trumpet-like megaphone when he sights a shoal of pilchards; and see in your minds eye the hustle and bustle as all the local folk excitedly echo the cry and began to prepare for the landing of the catch, and watch the Huer's semaphore instructions (a bit like those used by ground crew to direct modern aircraft taxiing in after flight) with hand held bushes to the fishing boats, as they hastily respond to his call from the top of the hill. If you have worked up a healthy appetite on the attractive coastal walk in that region and climbed the hill to examine the ruined hut, you will not need much imagination to believe that you can smell the cake baked in celebration by the fishwives when the cry signalled the approaching shoals of pilchards and anticipated activity for the whole family and community. Every able bodied person would be involved in dealing with the pilchards which they had been eagerly awaiting - even quite small children would fetch and carry packs of salt etc, to the women who would be busy preparing and packing the fish. Large shoals of pilchards would come only a few times a year if they were fortunate. They would not only be eaten locally, but salted, cured, pressed and packed for transport elsewhere, or for later local consumption. Nothing would be wasted. The pilchard oil would be collected to be used to light lamps and stoves, and waterproof their clothing (Hence the word 'oilskins'); anything which could not be otherwise used was sold for fertiliser on the fields.

Stories of smuggling and wreckers and other colourful folklore abound over the whole South West Peninsular. They have been found to be good for tourism and many communities are cashing in on this where they can. For all that the region has to offer in beauty and interest, it still has to compete with cheap holidays abroad. Many fishing folk, as their ancestors before them turned to smuggling, now have to turn to tourism either to supplement their income by using their boats for tourists' angling or sightseeing trips or they may have completely forsaken fishing for reasons given above. An increasing number of smuggling connections are being claimed, and the colourful characters of the past have again become household names but less fearfully and disreputably than before. The same names and often similar stories appear connected with different places. Similarly we were also amused to find that Dartmouth, Plymouth and Newlyn all claim to be the place whence the Pilgrim fathers set sail. Dartmouth claiming that they only put into Plymouth to effect repairs and Newlyn claiming that they really set out from Newlyn after taking on water there!!

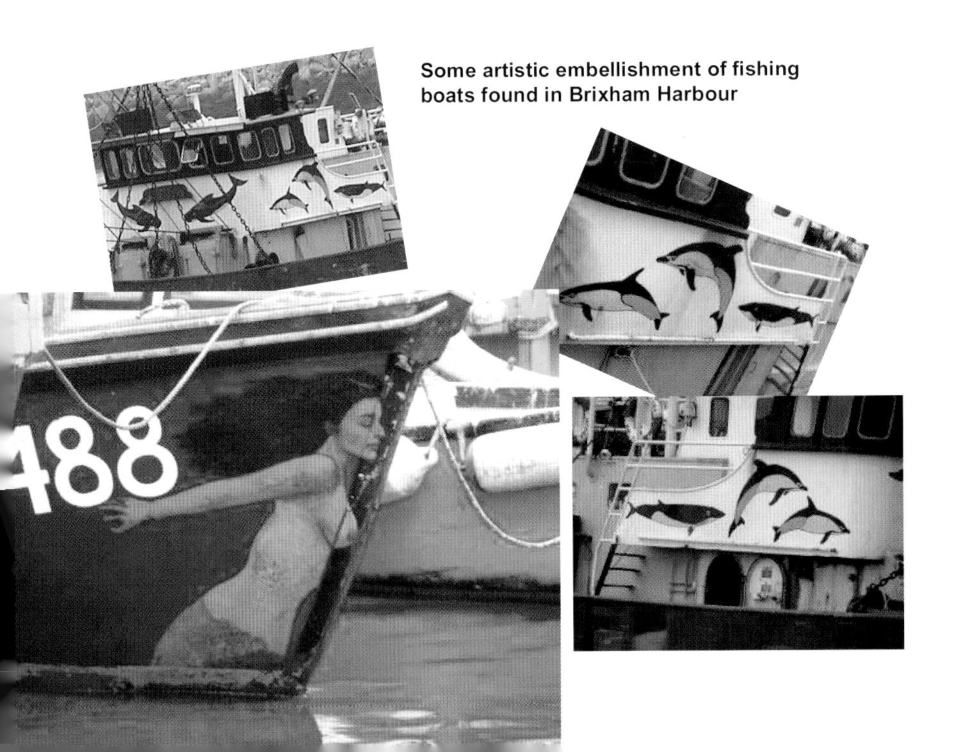

Some artistic embellishment of fishing boats found in Brixham Harbour

Over the years fishing methods have developed differently between Devon & Cornwall. The powerful Brixham trawler gaff rigs were well known, and the trawlers in the North East owed their origin to the Brixham design. The method of beam trawling was also exported from the South West. The percentage of trawlers is greater in Devon fleets than Cornwall, while there are a higher proportion of netters in Cornwall although the small boat potting and netting around local areas is similar in both counties. Fishing trawlers traditionally made use of the lugsail or 'Dandy' rig (a combination of gaff and lugsails) as its good windward performance made possible faster passages from the fishing grounds to local fish markets. The time taken to get a catch to market was further improved when the railways reached Exeter and further to Exmouth, allowing fish landed in Devon to be even in London markets within 24 hours of being caught.

Historic Brixham Trawler

Much has been happening in recent years to preserve the memory of the splendid historical Brixham trawler At one time Brixham had one of the world's largest fleets of wooden sailing trawlers and was indeed the birthplace of these graceful yet powerful fishing boats, which were built in local yards (though the town of Beer lays some claim to this). Unlike other fishing vessels at the time they were capable of towing heavy trawl gear in all conditions yet they were unmatched in speed by any other fishing boats. This made them highly successful in the important competition to get fish to market quickly while still fresh. Unlike today's larger modern trawlers which can stay at sea fishing for days, they had no refrigerated holds in which to store fish - although some did carry large blocks of ice which had been brought from Scandinavia packed in straw for the purpose. Their successful design spread throughout the world. It is estimated today that there exist only about fourteen traditional Brixham Sailing Trawlers worldwide and happily more of them are being seen again in their native Brixham thanks to the volunteer efforts of Brixham sailing trawler enthusiasts and a few notable restoration projects like the Trinity Sailing Foundation, Pilgrim Trust, and Vigilance preservation society. Several of these restored traditional trawlers Pilgrim, Vigilance, Provident, Keywardin, Golden Vanity, Regard, and Leader can often be seen in the Torbay area and sometimes further a field, and most of them can be found from time to time moored in Brixham harbour on the Town Pontoon. Together with other traditional fishing vessels of all classes they can also be seen competing for the Kings Cup in the annual Brixham Heritage Festival race usually held on May Spring Holiday Saturday. Modern Trawlers also race over that weekend. If your desire is to experience first hand the conditions sailing aboard a traditional Brixham Trawler this experience is offered by Trinity Sailing Holidays (www.trinitysailing.co.uk, www.vigilanceofbrixham.co.uk and www.regardofbrixham.co.uk). Should you wish to find out about the history of any Brixham Sailing Trawler the Brixham Heritage Sailing Trawlers Archive contains the record of all the boats built in Brixham and enables searches by boat name or number, owner or skipper (www.brixham.uk.com/history/trawlers.htm).

Modern Trawlers at Brixham Heritage Weekend Event (DL)

Something which might capture your imagination about fishing boats is their names, if like us you cannot resist wondering how the names of places, houses, and boats came about. You may find that many boats bear the names of the owner's children such as Boy Karl, Girl Jean, but GARN (E4 Budleigh Salterton) had us puzzled, until the owner explained that he had intended to call his boat GAR making use of the initial letters of the names of his three children, but then his first grandchild put in an appearance and so the boat was called GARN. We did not ask if he would be forced to keep adding letters or perhaps buy another boat if he had any more grandchildren! The many female names of boats, which traditionally are addressed as feminine, made us hope for their owner's sakes, like the many bearers of tattoos, that this was still the name of the current girl friend or wife – particularly if the owner was one who held a superstition about changing a boat's name. We found 'My Gal' which might be a way around this difficulty and be sufficiently ambiguous as possibly to refer to the boat alone. 'CAWTE 1' struck us as being particularly apt. We discovered that this boat with registration number FY 835, only after much fruitless searching, had been decommissioned . We have managed to photographically capture around 1,250 boats, about 550 of them in Devon - some of them several times with improved or updated shots (perhaps after repainting). The ultimate aim has been to photograph the boats at sea on the water which should give a better representation of how they would appear to safety or emergency personnel attempting identification. This has meant that reluctantly much otherwise good photography has been removed from the 'active' collection, when a boat was initially seen ashore or moored up alongside.

In this introduction only a few of the wonderful places and interesting facts that can be discovered on a 'Fishing Boat' or 'Fishing Port' hunt around Devon have been highlighted to whet your appetite, because we hope that you will want to make the discovery for yourself. Enjoy your voyage of coastal discovery, which will bring you back over and over again, because visiting in different seasons, and different states of tide and weather, will all influence the number of fishing boats seen, as well as the appearance of their surroundings.

The more you see of this wonderful coastline the more you will want to explore further round the coast, and then you will want to marvel at the changes that the different seasons bring. Obviously fewer people tour this region in the winter and yet the climate is mild and there is so much more to be seen passing through the countryside, without the leaves on the trees obscuring the wider picture. The coastline of this South West Peninsular has been considered by many to be amongst the finest in the world - a reputation which in our opinion it well deserves.

Elizabeth Lenton

The Devon Belle taken from the Dartmouth Ferry

Examples of Changes in Fishing Boat Appearance

All these are the same boat - Spot the differences

New Colour Scheme for BM4

02/03/2005

04/02/2006

New colour scheme & name change
E495 SOPHIE of LADRAM to E495 AMY-R

08/11/2003
E495 SOPHIE of LADRAM

04/02/2006
E495 AMY-R

E14 Heart of Oak - Masts removed & new colour scheme

7/05/04

20/07/05

All these are the same boat - Spot the differences

AH101 Girl Soo

30/12/04

13/05/05
Addition of Wheelhouse & change of colour

29/03/06
New colour scheme

All these are the same boat - Spot the differences

BM19 Sea Otter - Registration Number & Colour Change

06/04/04
As BM19 Sea Otter
Blue Hull

23/02/05
As DS7 Sea Otter
Red Hull

01/02/06
As BM222 Sea Otter
Red Hull

All these are the same boat - Spot the differences

Colour Changes to PH277 Chiltern Boy

16/09/05
White Hull

11/07/05
Dark Blue Hull

11/05/06
Yellow Hull

All these are the same boat - Spot the differences

CF1 Nemesis - Colour Scheme

03/08/03
Blue Hull

01/04/05
Red Hull

09/08/06
Blue Hull

Examples of Changes in Fishing Boat Appearance

All these are the same boat - Spot the differences

SS150 Bethany Colour

17/11/04
Red
In Plymouth
(Sold when all pots stolen)

10/02/06
Black
In Teignmouth
Sold again

03/07/06
Blue
In Beer

THE FISHING VESSELS AND PORTS IN DEVON

The fishing industry, in Devon and Cornwall together, accounts for approximately half the entire fish landings in England, in terms of both quantity and value, and although there has been a gradual decline in the fishing industry generally, the decline has been less marked in the West Country, which is fortunate in having a rich variety of fish in its waters. There are seven main types of fishing vessels. A brief description of each follows.

Multi Purpose Trawlers These trawlers are the mainstay of the inshore fishing fleets and are used mainly to catch demersal fish on the sea bed. The bag-like conical trawl net is streamed on two lines attached to heavy boards, known as 'Otter Boards' which are towed at an angle such that they hold the trawl net open. The top of the net is attached to buoyancy to keep it from the bottom. In port or in transit the otter boards will be seen, usually suspended externally, on the aft ends of the vessels on both sides. Small derricks are usually fitted to handle them and powerful winches are needed to haul in the trawl net. The trawl will be between 1/4 mile and 1 mile in length depending on the size of vessel and may be carried out at a variety of depths depending on the target species. It is towed at a speed of 2- 3 knots. When trawling, the boats are very restricted in manoeuvrability, with only small changes in direction possible, since otherwise the otter boards will be pulled close together thus closing the net. When the trawl is lowered to the sea bed to catch demersal fish it is referred to as 'Otter Trawling', and, when the trawl is between the surface and the sea floor to catch pelagic fish, it is referred to as 'Mid Water or Pelagic Trawling'. The depth of the trawl is then controlled by controlling the length of haul line or the speed of advance. A 'Twin Rig Trawler' is capable of pulling two trawl nets with a third central haul line attached to both of the nets while the outer lines with the otter boards keep the nets open and apart. They are usually used for trawling on the sea bed. A 'Pelagic Trawler' pulls one very large trawl net which is kept open laterally by the otter boards and vertically by weights pulling the bottom of the Trawl downwards. It is used for catching mackerel and Herring and requires very powerful vessels. When two trawlers act together towing one trawl net between them it is known as 'Pair trawling'. The heavy otter boards to keep the net open are no longer required, and because of the extra motive power available they can pull a larger net, and are also more manoeuvrable. They have had a lot of bad press recently due to the number of dolphins which have been trapped in the larger trawl nets. The boats generally have a crew of between two and four and will usually stay at sea for less than 24 hours.

Figure 1

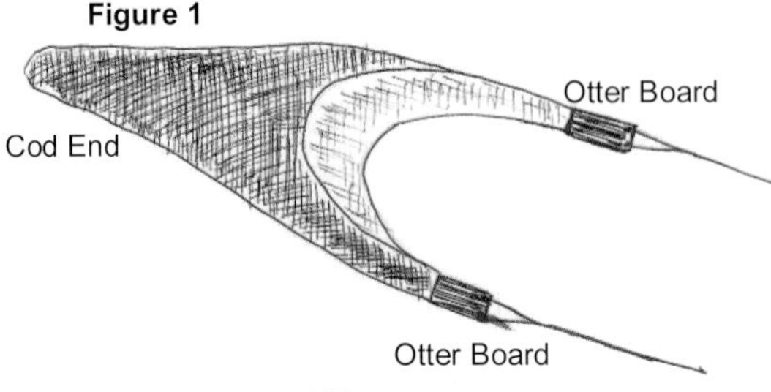

\Diagram of a Trawl Net

Beam Trawlers Beam trawling is a very efficient way of catching flat fish such as plaice, sole, turbot or brill. The bag like trawl nets are attached to heavy metal bars (Beams), which are suspended from derricks (booms) on each side of the vessel, lowered down (called 'shooting the nets') and dragged along the sea bed. The ends of the beams keep the net open and they can be towed at speeds up to 7 knots and so require considerable power. Without the restriction of the otter boards, they are not restricted to fishing in straight lines as the trawlers above. They can also be used for shrimp trawling with lighter gear and at slower speeds. Generally they will trawl at depths up to 600ft, but it is possible to trawl at depths up to 4,000ft. The nets will be left down for up to two hours and then hauled. Beamers are generally larger boats and will often remain at sea for up to ten days. Unfortunately the gear can weigh up to 10 tons, and being so heavy it can leave considerable damage to the sea bed in their path. Coal 'caught' amongst the catch is not unknown and it may be bagged and sold. Deploying the booms out provides additional stability to the trawlers and even when in transit they will have them lowered out horizontally on each side.

Beam Trawl Nets and Explanatory Diagram below

Figure 2

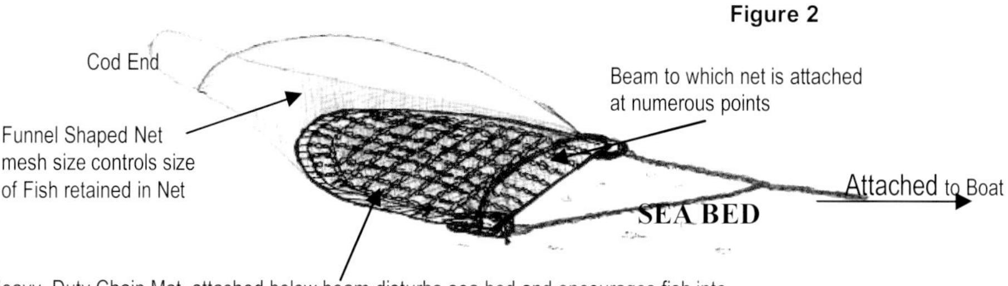

Scallopers These have similar equipment to the beam trawler but on a smaller and lighter scale, and instead of one net they have several scallop dredges which have rings or spikes to rake the seabed and net or metal bags to catch the scallops or shellfish as they are raked up Smaller vessels may have as few as three or four net dredges on each side while the larger vessels may have sixteen or more per side. Some vessels are designed solely for scalloping but many of the beam and general purpose trawlers can be quickly modified in port to carry the scallop dredgers. Scallops can be dredged from depths up to 90 fathoms but the deeper scallops tend to be smaller and less tasty. Scallop fishing is popular because there is a ready and lucrative market and there are no official quotas.

Figure 3

A Scallop Dredge - Crown copyright reproduced with permission

Figure 4

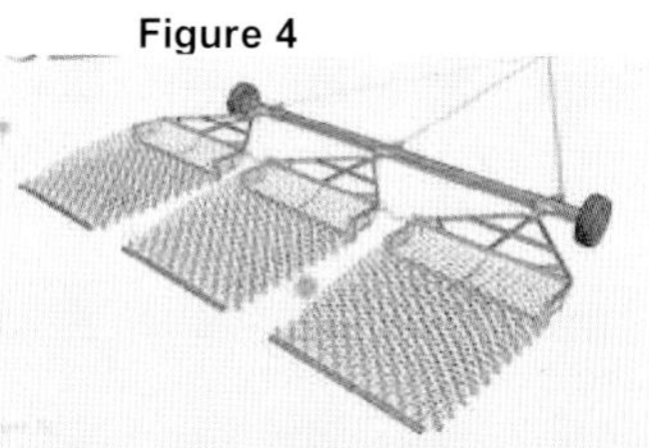

Several Dredges Shackled to the Beam - Crown copyright reproduced with permission

Each dredge is fitted with a chain and bridle to attach it to the beam, and the whole assembly towed on a single wire warp. The vessels tow two beams, one on each quarter, and the number of dredges on each varies according to the towing power and manoeuvrability in the prevailing weather conditions. See picture on page xxii of CO365 Celtic Pride with beams and dredges deployed.

BM249 Trawler rigged with 12 Scallop Dredges (CF1 on page xvii also illustrates these)

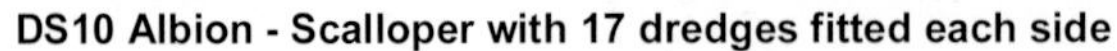

DS10 Albion - Scalloper with 17 dredges fitted each side

Scalloper DS 10 illustrated above also shows part of a mechanism that some of the larger scallopers have for emptying the dredges of scallops. The area of the side of the boat which appears rusty in the picture above rotates upwards and 'teeth' attached to it catch on the scallop dredges forcing them to turn upside down emptying the scallops (and any other 'catch'- stones, fish etc.) on to a conveyor belt or hoppers inside the boat.

CO365 - Celtic Pride with deployed beams with scallop dredges attached

Scallop dredges are changed according to the types of scallops which are to be fished. Queen scallops are smaller (around 3" across) as illustrated in the pictures on the right and below. They are also good swimmers which means that they can be trawled as well as dredged unlike their larger relatives which are poorer swimmers and tend to seek crevices in rocks from which they must be dredged.

Queen Scallop on the right

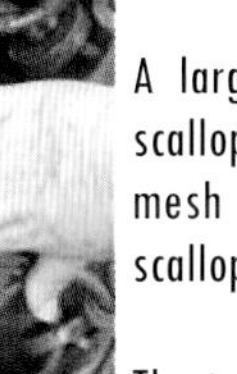

Scallop dredge on left & close up above

A larger ring mesh is used for the larger scallop illustrated on the left. A smaller ring mesh is employed in dredging for queen scallops which are known as 'queenies'.

The teeth on the rakes are set closer together or at smaller intervals apart on the bar when dredging for queen scallops (see picture on the left) The pictures below illustrate the wider apart teeth of the normal scallop dredges compared with those for 'queenies'.

A Pile of Queen Scallop rakes on the quayside waiting to be fitted.

A single scallop dredge dismantled to allow refitting gear for 'Queenies'

The larger scallop dredge in situ pictured to show the larger intervals between the teeth on rake

A well known scallop dish served in a scallop shell is Coquille (Scallop) St Jacques (St James). The scallop shell has always been associated with St James the Great. There are several legends attributing to the origin of this, including one stating that the horse carrying the Saint's remains from Jerusalem to Spain fell into the water and emerged covered in scallops. St Jame's shrine at Santiago de Compostela was the destination of many Medieval pilgrimages, and pilgrims to it wore a scallop emblem. The scallop later became associated with all Christian pilgrims. Probably because of this it has been incorporated in many coats of arms including those of the families of both Winston Churchill and John Wesley and thus the scallop shell also became the symbol of the Methodists.

" Give me my scallop-shell of quiet,
My staff of faith to walk upon,
My scrip of joy, immortal diet,
My bottle of salvation'
My gown of glory, hope's true gage;
And thus I'll take my pilgrimage. "

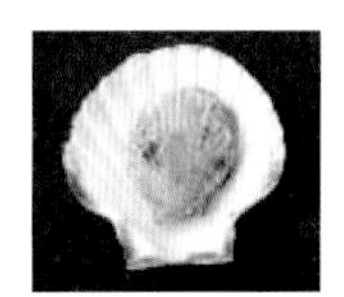

Queen Scallop inside

Thus wrote the great Elizabethan explorer and poet- Sir Walter Raleigh (1552-1618)

Gill Netters (Drifters) Drift netters carry a length of curtain like net which is let out (shot) from the stern and suspended from floats on the surface, as the boat travels downwind. The line holding the net is then taken round to the bow so that the drifter can lie head to wind. Tension is then kept on the line of net as the boat is blown downwind. Drift netters often carry a mizzen sail to help keep the boat into wind. Lengths of net vary but they may be several miles long in some cases. Such extreme lengths are unlikely to be used in the busy UK waters because of the risk of other vessels fouling the nets. The fish are caught by catching their gills in the nets and there are strict rules on the sizes of mesh netting to be used for the type of fish to be caught, and to ensure that only mature fish are caught and not the young. Gill nets may also be set on the bottom as shown and marked with buoys. The nets are hauled using equipment traditionally installed on the starboard side forward of amidships.

Figure 5

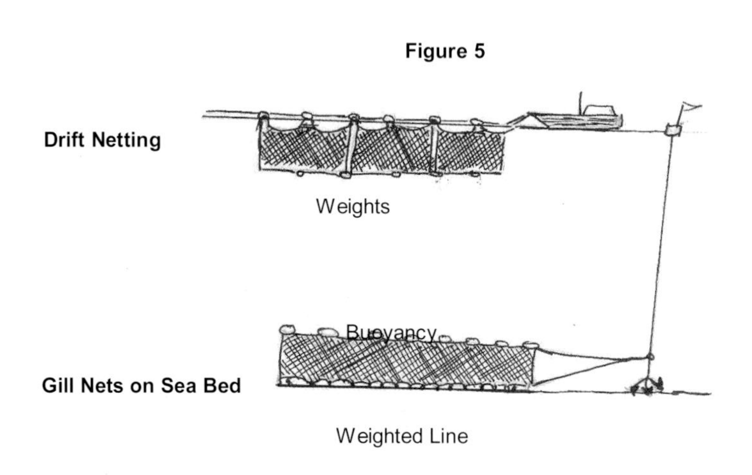

Purse Seiner/Ring Netters and Seine Netters These all have one thing in common in that, instead of waiting for the fish to swim into them, the gear is taken around a located shoal of fish to catch them.

Purse Seine/Ring Netters The net is shot round a located shoal in a circle. The net is then pursed (or closed) underneath the shoal by hauling in a wire which goes from the vessel through rings located at the bottom of the net and back to the vessel. The size of the purse is then reduced until the net is alongside and the fish are either scooped out called 'brailing' or pumped out using fish pumps. The timing of each part of the manoeuvre to prevent the shoal escaping is critical. The mesh used is very fine so that the fish caught within the net are undamaged.

Figure 6

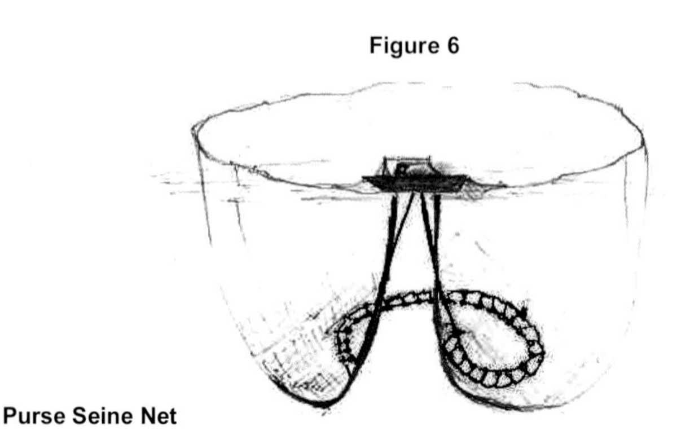

Seine netting This is a bottom fishing method particularly suited to flat sandy bottoms and is often used for demersal (ground fish) - cod, haddock and hake and flat-fish like plaice and flounder. The end of one towing warp is buoyed and dropped overboard. The fish are surrounded by motoring round the shoal in a large triangle as the warps (rope) are laid out on the seabed with a net with wings between them and returning to the buoyed warp (see fig 7) The boat then either anchors or moves slowly forward and as the warps are hauled in the fish are herded into the path of the net and caught. The warps' movement across the seabed results in a cloud of soft sediment, sand, or mud assisting the process. This method of fishing yields a better quality catch, as the fish are not jolted on the bottom as with trawling. It is also more economical on fuel.

Figure 7 A Modern Seine

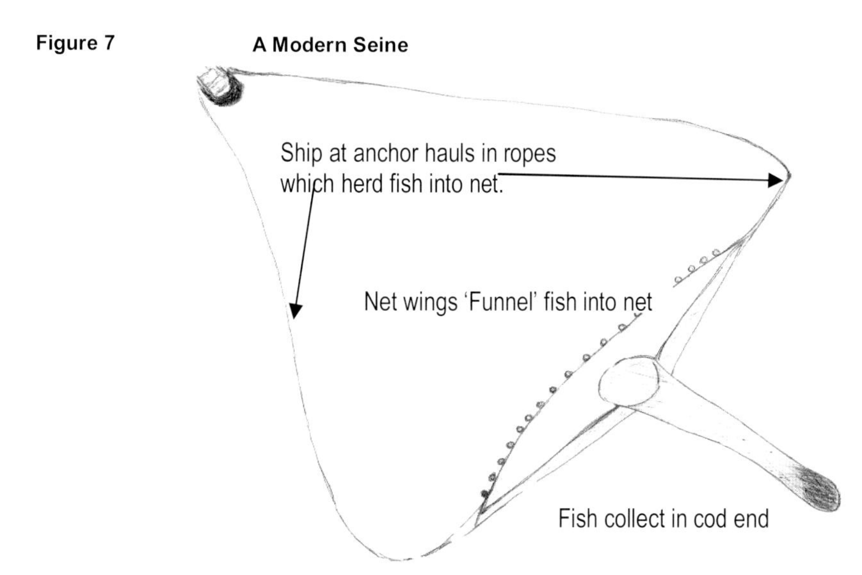

The seine, or dragnet is well documented in ancient writings for instance by Ovid and the Bible, and is depicted on ancient Egyptian grave paintings of the 3rd century BC. Thus it must be the oldest type of commercial fishing net. The basic method seems to have changed little over the centuries and Ovid mentions the use of corks to support the top and lead weights on the bottom. The greatest change seems to have come in the past century with the introduction of modern synthetic fibres.

> ***"Again, the kingdom of heaven is like a seine net which was thrown into the sea and gathered fish of every kind; when it was full, men drew it ashore and sat down, and sorted the good into vessels but threw away the bad."*** *(Matthew 13:47-48)*

Liners. 'Small Line fishing' may be carried out by hand or from poles suspended out from each side of the boat. Each line will carry several hooks on short branch lines called 'Snoods' which all have to be baited and laid out. It can be very hard work! The 'Longer Liners' require winch gear to haul in since they can have between 500 and 1,200 hooks spaced at one fathom (six feet) intervals. These are weighted at the bottom end to go down to, and along, the sea bed and may be left for several hours anchored with a marker dan buoy. Fish caught by netting often suffer gill damage which does not happen with fish caught on a hook, which is one advantage of line fishing. Fish so caught will be landed as quickly as possible. Most of the line fishing in the South West is 'Small or Long Lining' but 'Great Lining' uses much longer lines with up to 12,000 hooks and at depths up to 3000ft with fully mechanised baiting, shooting and hauling equipment. The small or hand liners generally use about 60 metre lines with snoods set at one metre intervals.

Potters, Crabbers and Whelkers These are vessels which have the ability to carry a number of pots or creels which are laid on a continuous line with a marker buoy left at each end. Pots can be ink bottle shaped as in figure 8 or as in the centre picture of the illustrations below, and are used mainly for crab. Creels are either rectangular or D-shaped as illustrated in the other pictures and are used for lobster. Crab require fresh bait whereas lobsters take stale bait. Whelks and prawn pots obviously must be of smaller mesh than those used for crab and lobster, and traditionally they were made of basket work. Today plastic, metal, wood and even polythene tubing might be used. The boats are fitted with a winch system to haul in the pots over some form of davit, usually fitted forward on the starboard side to keep the lines from the propeller. After leaving the baited pots down, ideally for about 24 hours, the pots are lifted in turn, the catch removed, pots re-baited and lowered back to the seabed again in one continuous action. Even small open boat potters may service as many as 250 pots while the larger potters may service as many as a 1,000 and possibly up to 2,000. These boats are often fitted with large trays on the transom to carry the pots and the larger vessels will carry them below decks as well. The type of pots and baits used depends on whether the boat is used for lobsters, crab or whelks. Lobsters will take stale bait but crabs require fresh.

Figure 8

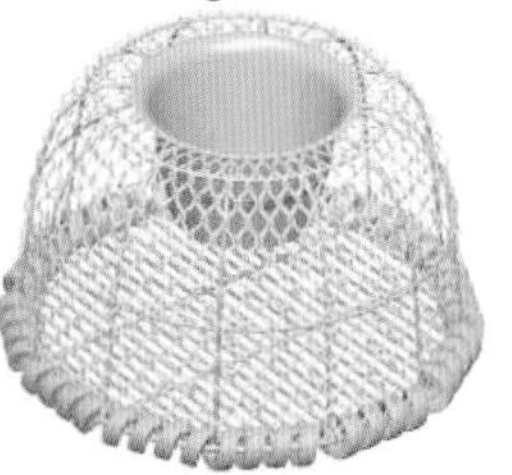

Examples of some of the Various styles of Pots & Creels that exist

Many of the modern vessels being built are designed as multi-purpose fishing vessels and can quickly be adapted to trawling, netting potting or lining.

Unloading the Pots

Historically, Devon's fleet was mainly based on trawling, catching demersal (ground) fish, rather than seine and drift netting aiming for pelagic (surface) fish, and although less marked, this situation has continued. The demersal fish include plaice, sole, turbot, cod, pollack, eels and ling, while pelagic fish include mackerel, pilchards, bass, herring and mullet. Devon has just under 400 active fishing vessels of which one third are trawlers, a quarter are netters, and just under a third are potters. The numbers have declined by about 5% over the past three years. The Devon figures include some 15 boats which operate out of Plymouth, but are based on the Cornish side of the River Tamar. (These boats are however featured in the Cornwall Book of ports and boats) Very few vessels are engaged solely in hand or long line fishing. The larger vessels are restricted by law from fishing close inshore to preserve stocks, so many of the smaller craft are able to take advantage of this by fishing inshore.

Simple Hogshead Press

Quarto Hogshead Packed

Until the 1930s much of the fishing industry in both Cornwall and South and North West Devon was based on the pilchard season. Huge pilchard shoals of up to 500,000 fish having wintered in the warmer waters west of the Scillies, moved north-eastwards in July, and on reaching Lands End split north and south, moving along the North and South coasts of Devon and Cornwall. Because of this slow advance, catches could be anticipated as the shoals moved along the coast. The method of catching the shoals was fascinating. They were caught using seine netting in groups of three boats. One larger vessel, the 'Seine', surrounded a shoal with the seine net, and dragged it into shallow water. The second smaller boat called the 'Follower' (sometimes corrupted as 'Vollier') carried the 'stop net' to go under the shoal and lift the fish from the water. To empty a well filled seine net could take several days, if not weeks. A third faster boat called the 'Huer' directed the operations, sometimes with semaphore assistance from lookout positions on the shore. Such a group was known as a 'Seine', and though most of them were in Cornwall, there were several along the South Devon coast as far as Torbay, and in the 19th century along the North Coast as far as Ilfracombe. The pilchard season lasted from July to October and in many years provided a sufficient income for the whole year in that period alone. Since the mackerel season was from January to June, this fitted in well with the July to October pilchard season. With the pilchards came the predatory and more valuable hake. These were caught by hand lining and made a profitable sideline to the main mackerel fishing. The photographs show the traditional methods of pressing and packing the fish which continued to be used in the last operational fish cellar in Newlyn, Cornwall until it sadly closed in November 1995. From the late 19th century, the pilchards ceased coming in such numbers, and drift netting, for both pilchards and mackerel, gradually took over from seine netting. The industry employed large numbers of people ashore, gutting, salting and packing the fish, and maintaining and building the boats and gear. Some of the historical fish cellars can still be found at the traditional fishing ports, though most in Devon have disappeared.

Pressed and ready for packing

Potting takes place all around the Devon coasts, but Salcombe, Beesands and Kingswear together, support the largest crab fishery in the UK accounting for about 15% of the total UK crab landings. The brown crabs and lobsters are mainly for UK consumption but most of the spider and velvet crabs are exported, and many are landed directly in France. Oyster fisheries have also been developed in the River Tamar, and there are

Important mussel beds in the rivers and estuaries of the Exe, Teign, Dart, Torridge and Taw, and at Kingsbridge in Devon. Scalloping is a lucrative feature of the South Coast fishing fleets and Plymouth is one of the main landing ports for scallops in the UK. Lyme Bay and the area around the Eddystone are particularly favourable for scalloping, though there is concern over the damage being caused to some fragile coral reefs in Lyme Bay. Many of the larger vessels alternate between trawling for white fish, and scalloping, while some vessels now specialise in scalloping alone. Several Scottish scallopers are frequent seasonal visitors to the area and can regularly be seen operating from Plymouth. Some of the visiting boats are listed in a separate section at the end of the book.

There are over sixty landing places, from which fishing vessels operate in Devon and Cornwall, and these are listed in clockwise order round the coast as shown on the map inside the front cover of this book .

Ex BM28 'Provident' by Plymouth Breakwater

Traditional Fishing boats at a Vintage Boat Rally in Plymouth Sound

ADMINISTRATIVE & REGISTRATION PORTS

Administrative Centres There are two Administrative Centre locations for fishing vessels operating in Devon, namely Brixham, and Plymouth. Working clockwise around the coast, Brixham covers the South Coast from Lyme Regis to Dartmouth; Plymouth covers Dartmouth to the River Tamar (and along the Cornish coast to Fowey), and the North Devon Coast from Clovelly to Bristol, and also some ports in South Wales. These Administrative Centres regulate catches and ensure adherence to the safety regulations which apply, increasingly, as the size of boat increases. Skippers of fishing vessels greater than ten metres length are required by law to keep a 24 hour log of their catches. These logs are presented to the local Fisheries Officer wherever the catch is landed, and copies of them are then sent on to the vessel's Administrative Centre. The choice of the vessel's Administrative Centre may just be at the request of an individual owner or skipper, and it is quite possible for a vessel operating in the South West to use a centre completely outside the area. This applies particularly when some boats visit the area for a particular fishing season from as far away as Scotland. For these reasons, boats, although operating from the same port, may be using different Administrative Centres.

Skippers/Owners of fishing vessels less than ten metres registered length, while not obliged by law to keep a record of their catches, usually do, although they do not have to submit them to the Administrative Centres. This is why so many boats are coming into service specifically designed to be just under ten metres registered length. Ten metres is also the size above which even more stringent equipment and safety regulations apply. (15 metres length is the next step up, where even further regulations apply). Because the registered length is measured from the bow of the boat to the stern post (where the rudder is mounted), there are several boats with an overall length of more than ten metres, but which are still registered as vessels of ten metres or less. Many owners of smaller boats have difficulty, financially and physically, installing the requirements for boats of ten metres and under into their smaller hulls, and many such owners believe that there is a case for less stringent regulations for vessels of say under six metres length.

Registration Ports The Ports of Registration round the coast are those ports which have been centres of fishing activities around the coasts historically and were also the Custom House Ports for the area. Any fisherman wishing to obtain a licence to operate from a particular port will generally be granted a licence by DEFRA with a number following the letters of the nearest Registration Port. These numbers and letters are painted on the sides of the hull at bow and stern and also on part of the structure facing upwards, to be visible from the air.

The idea of fishing vessels carrying an identifying number started in about 1840 at the end of the war with France. There was still considerable friction between French and English fishing vessels in the English Channel, and to enable the military to recognise and identify English fishing vessels it was agreed that they should display the first and last letters of their nearest Customs Port followed by an identifying number. This produced some anomalies however as places like Poole and Penzance, Portsmouth and Plymouth for example had the same first and last letters. In 1869 some of the anomalies were sorted out by a Merchant Shipping Act which resulted in Penzance taking the letters 'PZ' and Portsmouth a single letter 'P'. This same Act divided fishing vessels into three classes. A first class boat was over 15 registered tons and had the port letters before the number. Second class boats were sailing vessels under 15 registered tons and had the numbers before the port letters, while third class boats were essentially rowing vessels which like the first class boats had the letters before the number, the size difference differentiating between them.

Individual Customs Officers allocated the numbers in their own ways however, resulting in further confusion. In St Ives boats of any class were numbered numerically such that a first class vessel might have SS1, a second class 2SS, and a third class SS3, while Penzance numbered each class numerically so that one could have PZ1, 1PZ and PZ1 again for a third class vessel. Lapsed numbers were allowed to be reissued and this resulted in several boats having the same number. Further difficulties occurred in the 1870s when steam vessels were introduced, and the machinery space reduced the vessels registered tonnage, forcing these more modern boats to be registered as second class, to the disgust of the proud owners. Steam vessels were therefore allowed to use gross tonnage. In about 1902 the system that we now have was formalised by Act of Parliament, and the three classes of vessels were dropped. DEFRA has since taken over the issue of permits. The early registers included details of the type of fishing boat and how many crew, but these details are no longer listed. Some of the registration ports still have boats on their registers even though very little, or even no, fishing activity continues from them. Barnstaple (BE) is an example where there is very little activity, but they still have a few boats registered, while Exeter (E), although having quite a large registered fleet, boats cannot even get up the River Exe as far as Exeter. Now any fisherman wishing to obtain a licence to operate from a particular port will generally be granted a licence by DEFRA with a number following the letters of the nearest Registration Port. If they wish to reuse an old number, they have to be able to prove that the old number is no longer in use.

The Port of Registration is not necessarily the port from which the vessel operates, since as a boat gets bought and sold, the licence is often sold with it, and the boat continues under its old registration at the port of the new owner. Many owners prefer to keep a shorter number rather than re-register with a longer number. Also the cost of repainting the numbers in five locations on the hull can outweigh the cost of re-registration!. Some just feel it is unlucky to change the number! This explains why so many boats that are permanently based locally can be found with port registrations from beyond the South West. The registration letters of ports within Devon and Cornwall are listed below in Fig 9, and the registration letters of the other port registrations can be found in the overall list of boats at the end of this book, which is in alpha-numerical order of registrations.

Figure 9

E	Exeter	**PH**	Plymouth	**SC**	Isles of Scilly
TH	Teignmouth	**FY**	Fowey	**SS**	St Ives
DH	Dartmouth	**TO**	Truro	**PW**	Padstow
BM	Brixham	**FH**	Falmouth	**BD**	Bideford
SE	Salcombe	**PZ**	Penzance	**BE**	Barnstaple

Details of Devon's ports and the fishing vessels which can be found in them, follow in clockwise order round the coast,
starting at Clovelly in North Devon, and after Lynmouth going down to the South Coast at Seaton, finishing at Plymouth .
(See the map inside the front cover of this book).

43 CLOVELLY

Clovelly Breakwater

Clovelly Harbour

The first pier and fish cellars were donated by a local squire and completed by 1601. The pier was later extended in the 1820s. Clovelly then became one of the few sheltered harbours on the North Devon Coast, although it dries out completely at low water. The fishing industry then became more important than agriculture for its survival, until the recent advent of tourism. To a large extent the fishing depended on the herring season. When the herring shoals came up from the South West along and beyond the Cornish coast during the 18th and 19th century, catches were sufficient to provide for many of the North Devon towns and villages round Bideford bay. Some Clovelly herrings were exported to South Wales from Bideford. It is the only village in Britain which is inaccessible to motor vehicles due to its steep, narrow, cobbled high street lined with attractive cottages. The packhorse, the donkeys, and the sledges pulled over the cobbles are still a feature of Clovelly, and the main street is aptly named 'Up Along' or 'Down Along'. There are still a few fishing craft netting for herring in the autumn season, and potting for crab and lobster all year round, and some charter fishing is also carried out in the tourist season.

Lined up on the Beach

The beer arrives by sledge

CLOVELLY FISHING VESSELS

Photo	Reg	VESSEL NAME	Type	LOA Mtrs	Reg Tons	Eng KW	Year Built	Hull	Nat Build
p	BD69	NEPTUNE	Angler	6.40	2.1	6	1970	W	GBR
p	BD279	CERI-LEE	Potter	4.45	0.9	5	1989	F	GBR
p	Ex BD290	MERMAID	De-registered	4.88			2005	F	GBR
p	BD292	BOMBAY	Potter	4.50			2005	F	GBR
p	PH477	HOOKER	Angler	8.00	5.2	134	1982	F	GBR
p	PZ778	NAOMI G	Potter	4.48	0.7	11	1992	F	GBR
p	SM77	LINDY LOU	Potter	4.27	0.8	7	1989	G	GBR
p	Ex TT254	BAIN HOPE	De-registered	9.6	3.6	275	1998	F	GBR

CLOVELLY

BD69 Neptune - 19/09/2005

BD279 Ceri-Lee - 19/09/2005

Ex BD290 Mermaid- 19/09/2005

BD292 Bombay - 19/09/2005

PH477 Hooker - 19/09/2005

PZ778 Naomi G - 19/09/2005

SM77 Lindy Lou - 19/09/2005

Ex TT254 Bain Hope - 19/09/2005

APPLEDORE

Appledore from Instow

River Torridge Estuary

Appledore, with its many historic attractive narrow streets and ancient buildings, is at the mouth of the River Torridge, where it joins up with the River Taw from Barnstaple, before flowing out into sea north of Westward Ho. Some fishermen's cottages date back to Elizabethan times. The Town Quay, against which most of the larger vessels moor up, was built in 1840. Before that the cottages and gardens dropped down to the water's edge. Appledore was granted the status of a 'Free Port' in recognition of the men and ships provided to defeat the Spanish Armada. This means that the locals do not have to pay any mooring fees! Several boats moor out in the river and some over the far side at Instow. Just up river from the town is one of the few still active ship building yards, making military vessels for the MOD, the largest being the survey ship HMS Scott, 13,300 tons, built in 1997. Alongside it is another yard employed in both building new fishing vessels and refitting older boats. Just beyond that is the landing place for the whelkers with a small processing plant. The shipbuilding yard has detailed records of all the craft built since the early 19th century. All types of boats operate from here, netting, trawling and potting and whelking, and mussel dredging occasionally takes place where the Rivers Taw and Torridge combine, using a dredger normally based at Exmouth. Not surprisingly the BD (Bideford) registration predominates. Many of the Bideford boats will often be seen at Appledore. Fish sales often take place at the quayside directly from the boats bringing in the catch. Fish cannot be bought any fresher than that!!

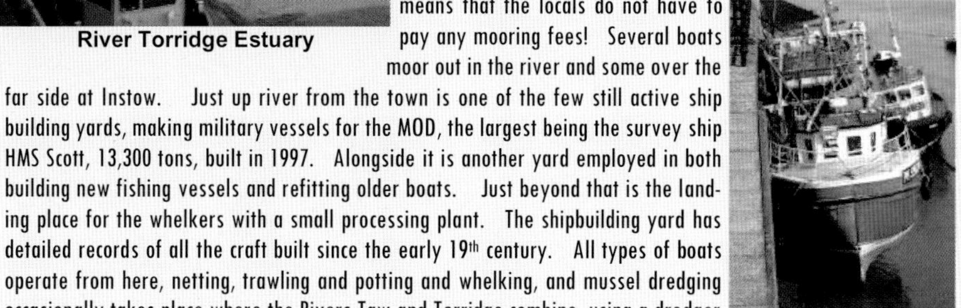

Against the Quay

APPLEDORE FISHING VESSELS

Photo	Reg	VESSEL NAME	Type	LOA	Reg	Eng	Year	Hull	NAT
				Mtrs	Tons	KW	Built		Build
p	BD1	CERULEAN	Trawler	14.98	33.7	298	2005	S	GBR
p	BD9	ANNA	Netter	7.60	6.1	62	1983	F	GBR
p	BD10	ESTRELA Do MAR	Potter	8.00	5.1	134	1992	F	GBR
p	BD76	BOY LEE	Trawler	9.75	9.3	119	1986	F	GBR
p	BD247	SEAPROSE	Trawler	9.91	5.9	89	1979	S	GBR
p	Ex BD282	ARGO	De-registered	<10					
p	Ex BD291		De-registered	<10					
p	BD297	SELACHOS	Angler	5.95	2.3	52	1998	F	GBR
p	BE29	K-SANDS	Netter	3.8		3		W	GBR
p	BE85	JACK	Netter	4.1	0.7	11	1998	F	
p	Ex BM290	SANDRA C	De-registered	5.7	1.7	30		F	GBR
p	K1126	COEL NA MAR	Whelker	11.00	18.1	134	1988	F	
p	NN147	DUCHESS	Trawler	9.14	7.18	89	1972	F	GBR
p	NN734	WINTER'S TALE	Trawler	9.80	12.61	134	2003	S	GBR

BD1 Cerulean - 14/01/2005

BD9 Anna - 02/08/2005

Ex BD10 Estrela Do Mar- 14/01/2006

BD76 Boy Lee - 02/08/2005

BD247 Seaprose - 02/08/2005

BE29 K-Sands - 14/01/2005

Ex BE85 Jack - 11/05/2005

Ex BM290 Sandra C - 19/09/2005

K1126 Coel Na Mar - 02/08/2005

NN147 Duchess - 14/01/2006

NN734 Winter'sTale - 09/12/2005

Landing the Catch

45 BIDEFORD

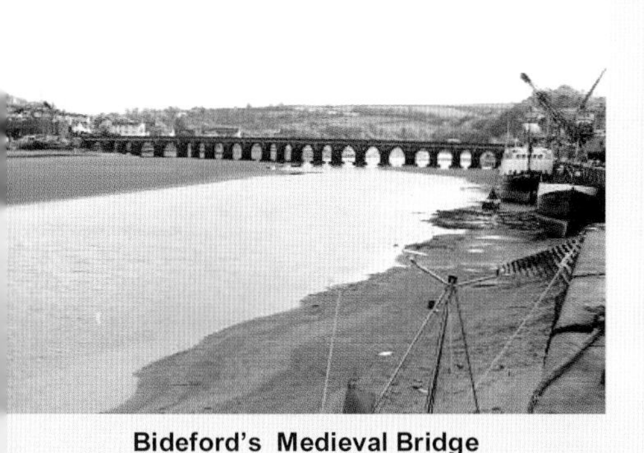

Bideford's Medieval Bridge

Vessels leaning against the Quay
Viaduct in the distance

Bideford town is at the position nearest to the sea where it was possible to ford the River Torridge . It was an important trading port being quoted as the third most important British port in the 17th century, especially with the import of tobacco from the States, coal from South Wales, and the export of wool. One hundred years later, the export of herrings which were originally landed at Clovelly is also recorded. It is still an active commercial port. The present 24 arched bridge which was widened in 1925 dates back to 1535, and replaced a wooden bridge first built in 1280. The relatively new bypass viaduct, seen in the picture on the right above has taken the pressure off the old bridge. Bideford is still a commercial port and has a regular ferry service across to Lundy Island. Some fishing vessels moor up against the 17th century town quay, just below the bridge, which dries out completely at low water. The River Torridge is an important salmon river and some salmon netting boats were registered locally, an example being B14 *(first boat listed over)* registered in Bideford, and there are others at the Maritime Museum in Appledore.

BIDEFORD FISHING VESSEL LIST

Photo	Reg	VESSEL NAME	Type	LOA Mtrs	Reg Tons	Eng KW	Year Built	Hull	NAT Build
p	B14	(Unnamed)	Salmon Netter	<5				W	GBR
	BD89	KYLIE MAY		4.08	0.6	3	0	W	GBR
	BD128	GLADYS JEAN		4.00	0.5	7	1989	F	UNK
p	Ex BD220	LUNDY STAR	De-registered	8.03	6.3	134	1985	F	UNK
	BE13	CARLA JANE		4.54	0.4	2	1982	W	GBR
p	GY165	PACEMAKER	Trawler	16.5	49.0	185	1970	W	GBR
p	PH58	BRUNO OF SUTTON	Trawler	15.08	20.5	215	1978	W	GBR
p	PH5562	HELCON	Trawler	9.95	4.5	82	1979	F	UNK
p	PW150	JEAN HOWARD	Trawler	11.22	23.9	134	1969	W	GBR
p	WK349	STEPHANIE	Trawler	13.70	21.9	179	1980	F	GBR
p	YH1	PIONEER	Netter	9.20	5.71	55	-	G	

B14 (Unnamed) - 02/08/2005

BD220 Lundy Star - 02/08/2005

GY165 Pacemaker - 14/01/2006

PH58 Bruno of Sutton - 14/01/2006

Old Trading Schooner by Bideford Bridge

BIDEFORD

PH5562 Helcon - 26/01/2005

PW150 Jean Howard - 11/05/2005

WK349 Stephanie - 14/01/2006

YH1 Pioneer - 14/01/2006

46 BARNSTAPLE

Barnstaple's Main Quay and 'Long Bridge'

Barnstaple's history as one of the most important market towns and ports in North Devon dates back to 930AD when it was established as a borough. It became a major port principally for the export of wool in the Middle Ages, and the 'Long Bridge' crossing the River Taw was built in the 15th century. Like Appledore it is another 'Free Port' in recognition of the five ships and crew provided to help defeat the Spanish Armada. Its importance as a port declined as the River Taw silted up. Despite being a fishing registration port there are few boats on the register and little fishing is carried out from here. Only two of the boats have been found, and they can be found moored either opposite the main quay below the bridge, or in the small creek leading off from the northern end of the main quay with a modern swing bridge at its entrance.

BARNSTAPLE FISHING VESSELS

Photo	Reg	VESSEL NAME	Type	LOA Mtrs	Reg Tons	Eng KW	YEAR BUILT	Hull	NAT Build
	BE3	DOLPHIN		6.00	1.1	88	1985	F	GBR
p	BE6	OTTER	Netter	4.40	0.7	5	0	W	GBR
	BE31	TANYA		5.07	0.6	2	1962	W	GBR
p	DR120	TOUCH of MADNESS	Netter/Liner	6.43	1.4	11	1983	F	GBR

BE6 Otter- 19/09/2005

DR120 Touch of Madness - 19/09/2005

47 ILFRACOMBE

The Inner Harbour

Harbour Entrance

Prior to the 19th century, Ilfracombe was just a small fishing village which was able to take advantage of the shoals of pilchards moving up from the southwest. As the shoals decreased in size they failed to reach this far up the coast in any significant numbers, and fishing declined. The port as well as being a useful shelter on the North Devon Coast, later became established as a popular Victorian destination for trippers from South Wales and a departure point for those going to Lundy Island. The pilot boats for the Bristol Channel also waited here. When the North Devon Railway reached the town in 1870 it became an even more popular tourist destination. Fishing has not played an important part in the port's development but has continued on a small scale throughout. The harbour wall enclosing the inner drying out harbour was completed in the early 19th century, and the latest improvements took place in 2001. There are now a few medium sized vessels operating from the port with whelking being an important feature. Some boats also used Watermouth - a deep inlet just three miles east of Ilfracombe - which provided more shelter, but this is no longer used by any registered boats.

Inner harbour looking West

ILFRACOMBE FISHING VESSELS

Photo	Reg	VESSEL NAME	Type	LOA Mtrs	Reg Tons	Eng KW	Year Built	Hull	Nat Build
p	B80	GREEN ISLE II	Whelker	11.50	16.0	94	1980	F	GBR
p	ExBD109	GEORGINA	De-registered	8.84	4.3	22	1954	W	GBR
p	BD277	OLIVIER BELLE	Trawler	14.95			2005	S	GBR
p	BD287	OUR JOSIE GRACE	Twin Rig Trawler	14.95	176.0	1764	2002	S	GBR
p	BD296	MARLIN	Out of Area	7.30	5.2	37	2004	F	GBR
p	M78	COMPASS ROSE II	Whelker	11.00	12.7	95	1974	F	GBR
p	PZ632	MACEREUX	Trawler	9.91	7.1	73	1978	F	GBR
p	WY1	WALRUS	Whelker	10.86	8.3	112	1989	S	GBR

B80 Green Isle - 30/04/2006

Ex BD109 Georgina - 18/03/2005

BD277 Olivier Belle - 30/04/2006

BD287 Our Josie Grace - 30/04/2006

BD296 Marlin - 25/07/2005

M78 Compass Rose - 25/07/2005

PZ632 Macereux– 30/04/2006

WY1 Walrus - 30/04/2006

48 LYNMOUTH

The Inner Harbour

Harbour Entrance

Lynmouth has a small sheltered drying out harbour beside the mouth of the Rivers West Lyn and East Lyn which join together just before the harbour at the end of two steep gorges. In the 18th and 19th centuries it was a small port exporting agricultural produce and oysters, and importing coal and limestone. Despite the disastrous floods of 1952 which killed 34 people, the village and harbour have survived well, and flood protection measures now keep the river away from the harbour. There are still three small registered fishing vessels, mainly engaged in potting and occasional netting and line fishing. Most of the catches are sold locally

LYNMOUTH FISHING VESSELS

Photo	Reg	VESSEL NAME	Type	LOA Mtrs	Reg Tons	Eng KW	Year Built	Hull	Nat Build
p	BE9	OCTOBER MORNING	Pot/Line/Angler	8.07	4	71		W	GBR
p	Ex BE83	KINGFISHER	De-registered	6.93	2.89	92	1997	G	
p	BE83	KINGFISHER	Potter			73		F	GBR
p	Ex PW96	JAN B	De-registered	7.32	3.6	34	1971	F	
p	TH21	EYECATCHER	Netter	5.70	1.27	29	1990	F	GBR

LYNMOUTH

BE9 October Morning – 30/04/2005

BE83 Kingfisher – 30/04/2006

Ex BE83 Kingfisher – 25/07/2005

Ex PW96 Jan B - 30/04/2006

TH21 Eyecatcher - 25/07/2005

The Flood Protection Walls

SEATON

Mouth of the River Axe

Seaton Bridge and Fish Quay

Seaton is situated at the mouth of the River Axe. The original harbour on the River Axe was Axmouth, one mile upstream from the river estuary. Historically Axmouth was the most important harbour in the South West, and since The Fosse Way ends at Axmouth it is probable that the Romans used it. Its use as a port declined after a landslip partially blocked the river in the 14th century and the river subsequently silted up because of this . The present fish landing area is situated at the mouth of the River Axe, at the eastern end of Seaton. Here the small sheltered estuary provides home to a diminishing number of fishing vessels. In mid 2005 there were only five registered boats operating. Most are engaged in netting and/or potting for crab and lobster; and charter angling is popular during the tourist season, particularly for bass. 'Betty's Boys' is also equipped with lightweight trawl netting and gear. Fishing vessels can often be found under construction for local ports, or undergoing maintenance in the boatyard just upstream of the road bridge. E520 'Mia B' was fitted out for use at Exmouth, and E523 'Good Life' and E524 'Shamrock' were completed in 2006 for Seaton itself. The road bridge was built in 1877 and is the oldest surviving concrete bridge in England. Boats can occasionally be found moored above it. The river entrance is very exposed to a southerly wind, and the weather frequently restricts access. In common with the majority of boats along this stretch of coast most of the Seaton boats carry the 'E' (Exeter) registration.

SEATON FISHING VESSELS

Photo	REG	VESSEL NAME	Type	LOA Mtrs	Reg Tons	Eng Kw	Year Built	Hull	Nat Build
p	Ex CA377	SHAMROCK	De-registered						
p	Ex E18	BARBARA MAE	De-registered	7.1	2.4	63	1983	F	GBR
p	E28	MY LADY	Potter	5.6	1.4	15			
p	Ex E47	SHEMARA	De-registered	6.9	3.0	40	1979	W	GBR
p	E94	SUNBEAM	Potter	6.5	3.7	13	1972	W	GBR
p	Ex E133	SHIRLEY ANN (Ex Beer)	De-registered	6.4	3.4	22	1968	W	GBR
p	Ex E256	MARTHA-D	De-registered	7.0	5.2	60	1965	W	GBR
p	Ex E274	DICKIE BIRD II	De-registered	6.2	2.8	11	1966	W	GBR
p	E487	BETTY'S BOYS	Potter/Trawler	6.52	2.72	22	1980	F	GBR
p	E513	OUTCAST	Potter	6.5	2.2	67	2003	F	GBR
p	E523	GOOD LIFE	Liner/Netter/Potter	5.5	2.1	16.5	2001	F	GBR
p	E524	SHAMROCK	Liner	5.94	1.5	66	1989	F	GBR
p	TH22	JODIE V	Angler	7.0			2005	F	GBR
p	WH26	CHARJON	Potter	4.58	0.85	1	1980	W	GBR

SEATON

Ex CA377 Shamrock - 14/02/2005

Ex E18 Barbara Mae - 19/03/2006

E28 My Lady - 13/08/2005

Ex E47 Shemara - 12/08/2005

E94 Sunbeam - 19/03/2006

Ex E133 Shirley Ann - 12/08/2005

Ex E256 Martha D - 14/02/2005

E274 Dickie Bird II - 14/02/2005

SEATON

E487 Betty's Boys - 20/06/2006

E513 Outcast– 14/02/2005

E523 Good Life - 20/06/2006

E524 Shamrock - 20/06/2006

TH22 Jodie V - 20/06/2006

WH26 Charjon - 19/03/2006

Opportunities many times are so small that we glimpse them not and yet they are often seeds of great enterprises. Opportunities are also everywhere and so you must always let your hook be hanging . When you least expect it a great fish will swim by.

(Og Mandino - American essayist and Psychologist. 1923-1996)

BEER

Beer Beach looking South West

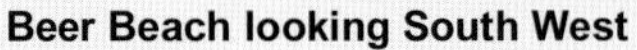

Beer Shingle Beach

Most of the Beer boats come under the Exeter umbrella, and have the 'E' registration. Despite the beach being completely exposed to the south it does have some shelter from the cliffs on both sides. Beer is still home to about half a dozen potters, which are winched back up the steep shingle beach. Charter angling is also popular in the tourist season, and there is still some hand lining for mackerel in season. The Beer word for a longline is a 'Bolty'. As a result of a hole in the cliffs being sealed with concrete at the east end of the beach the natural sea flow along the bay was disturbed such that the shingle beach has risen by some 8-10 feet in height since the 1980s, and pushed the shore line further from the slipway. The large capstan winch, which was used at the beach head, has now been repositioned as a monument above the fishing sheds. When a heavily laden boat came ashore it was necessary for up to eight of the locals to 'volunteer' to man the capstan to pull the boat ashore. Now each boat is required to have its own electric winch at the beach head to do the same job. The present raised beach provides more protection from the sea, but before the 1980s boats had to be hauled up almost to the level of the main road when southerly gales were expected. The area to the west of the slipway is known as 'Charlie's Yard'. Charlie was a woodworker who made all manner of repairs to the local boats. The 'Yard', a popular place for tourists to sit and watch the fishing activity, now has two memorial plaques to three fishermen who have lost their lives at sea in recent years, a reminder of just how dangerous the fisherman's life can be. On the other side of the slipway is the local fish shop from where many of the catches are sold. Beer was the last port to have 3-masted luggers, but it was by then a far cry from the days when the village supported a considerable fleet of some 20 small trawlers to rival Brixham.

CHARLIE'S YARD
AN AREA DEDICATED TO
ALL PAST FISHERMEN
WHO SAILED FROM
THIS BEACH
1979

Fresh Catch Ready for Sale

IN MEMORY OF
BEER FISHERMAN
JASON BEWICK
AGED 19 YEARS
SKIPPER OF THE TINA ANNE
LOST AT SEA
27-12-1985

IN
LOVING MEMORY
OF
SEAN AND ALI
LOST AT SEA
APRIL 1993

Beer fishermen maintain that trawling was introduced to Brixham from Beer, and since North Sea ports copied the Brixham methods, Beer was the original foundation for British trawling. Stone from the nearby Beer underground quarries was dragged down to Beer beach, loaded into barges, and taken to be used in the construction of several well known buildings including Exeter and St Paul's Cathedrals, Windsor Castle the Tower of London and Hampton Court. Beer's fishing history is closely rivalled by its history as a smuggling base!!

BEER FISHING VESSELS

Photo	Reg	VESSEL NAME	Type	LOA Mtrs	Reg Tons	ENG Kw	YEAR BUILT	HULL	Nat Build
p	E30	CYGNET	Out of Area	8.0	2.2	37	1996	F	GBR
p	E43	LILLIE MAY	Netter/Potter	5.5			2005	F	GBR
p	Ex E117	LIVELY LADY	De-registered	7.3	2.5	44	1981	W	GBR
p	E127	BARBARA JEAN	Potter	7.1	4.3	41	1974	W	GBR
p	E249	BLUE LADY	Potter	6.8	3.9	22	1979	W	GBR
p	Ex E271	BEE-J	De-registered	7.8	2.9	60	1975	W	GBR
p	E282	ADBRENAT	Potter	7.3	2.5	32	1980	W	GBR
p	Ex E289	PEARL	De-registered	6.8	2.6	22	1966	W	GBR
p	E515	SAMBE	Potter	8.0			2004	F	GBR
p	E527	ANNIE	Potter	5.5			2005	F	GBR
p	SS150	BETHANY	Netter/Potter	4.7	1.5	22	1982	F	GBR

E30 Cygnet - 20/06/2006

E43 Lillie May - 03/07/2006

Ex E117 Lively lady - 20/06/2006

E127 Barbara Jean - 03/07/2006

BEER

E249 Blue Lady - 24/05/2005

Ex E271 Bee J - 10/02/2004

E282 Adbrenat - 03/07/2006

Ex E289 Pearl - 19/03/2006

E515 Sambe - 03/07/2006

E527 Annie - 20/06/2006

SS150 Bethany– 20/06/2006

BRANSCOMBE MOUTH

Branscombe Mouth Shingle Beach

Branscombe Mouth is just two miles West of both Beer and the dramatic Hooken Cliffs which form an important part of the Jurassic Coastline. It is the site where a small stream reaches the sea at the shingle beach having passed through the steep valley of Branscombe itself. Despite the almost non stop tidal currents sweeping the steep shelving beach and its exposure to the prevailing south westerly winds, it has been a landing place for trade and fishing boats for centuries. Branscombe, originally called 'Vicarage' reflecting its original church ownership, is an attractive village straggling along the steep sided valley. Most of the fishing was carried out by part time farmers/fisherfolk. Smuggling also played a major part in the village trade in the early 19th century resulting in an 'Excisemen's Lookout' being built at Branscombe Mouth. Now a solitary potter operates from the beach.

BRANSCOMBE FISHING VESSEL

Photo	Reg	VESSEL NAME	Type	LOA Mtrs	Reg Tons	ENG Kw	YEAR BUILT	HULL	Nat Build
p	E293	BRANSCOMBE PEARL	Potter	6.5	2.2	30	1981	W	GBR

E293 Branscombe Pearl - 20/06/2006

Mouth of the River Sid

The Red Sandstone Cliffs Facing East

At the eastern end of Sidmouth town the tiny River Sid runs into the sea. It was a fairly important port until the river silted up making it unsuitable for navigation following severe storms and landslips in the 15th century. Some seine fishing was reported in the 1820s but now there are just a few netters and potters launched from the beach here, with an attractive backdrop of the red cliffs. All the boats are 'E' registered. Most of the boats are clinker built to withstand the rough usage incurred in dragging up and down the beach

SIDMOUTH FISHING VESSELS

Photo	REG	VESSEL NAME	Type	LOA Mtrs	Reg Tons	ENG Kw	Year Built	Hull	Nat Build
p	E9	STORMY DAWN	Potter	6.01	2.79	14	1968	W	GBR
p	E217	MARTA	Netter	4.0	0.6	11	1978	F	GBR
p	E284	SUNSHINE	Potter	5.6	1.2	14	1964	W	GBR
p	E457	FRANCIS B	Netter	5.0	0.8	19	1993	F	GBR
p	E460	GUS	Liner/Netter	5.15	1.14	19	1994	F	GBR
p	E519	RENE	Potter	5.5			2006	F	GBR

E9 Stormy Dawn - 2/07/2005

E217 Marta - 22/07/2005

E284 Sunshine - 22/07/20065

E457 Francis B– 14/07/2005

E460 Gus - 24/05/2005

E519 Rene - 20/06/2006

53 BUDLEIGH SALTERTON

Budleigh Salterton Beach & Cliffs

Shingle beach (Looking East)

Budleigh Salterton is just to the west of the mouth of the River Otter which being a shallow river was totally unsuitable for navigation. At one time the town was actually called 'Ottermouth', but gained its present name from the salt pans which were once a main industry of the town. Sir Walter Raleigh was born close to the town. The beach is unusual in having large shingle pebbles in contrast to the totally different red sandstone Jurassic cliffs on each side. Although several fishing boats are launched from the exposed beach in the centre of Budleigh Salterton, there are only a few registered boats amongst them, all once again engaged in local netting, and potting for crab and lobster, with the occasional hand lining trip. There are a number of unusual capstans and windlasses for winching the boats back up the shingle beach, which bear close inspection. All the boats are 'E' registered. Again most of the boats are clinker built to withstand beach launching.

BUDLEIGH SALTERTON FISHING VESSELS

Photo	REG	VESSEL NAME	Type	LOA Mtrs	Reg Tons	Eng Kw	Year Built	Hull	Nat Build
p	E4	GARN	Netter	4.8	0.8	13	2000	F	GBR
p	E25	OTTER	Netter	3.8	0.8	3	1988	F	GBR
p	E468	SALTY 1	Netter	4.4	0.9	14		F	
p	Ex E500	WOODY	De-registered	4.2	0.6			F	GBR
p	E505	STROMA	Netter/Potter	4.0	0.5			F	GBR

E4 Garn - 2/07/2005

E25 Otter - 22/07/2005

E468 Salty I - 22/07/2005

Ex E500 Woody - 22/07/2005

Old Capstan

E505 Stroma - 22/07/2005

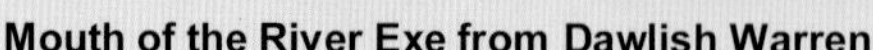

Mouth of the River Exe from Dawlish Warren

Exmouth Fish Quay

Historically the city of Exeter was the main port on the River Exe dating back to Roman times. Exmouth existed mainly as a ferry terminal across the Estuary between East and West Devon It was also a small fishing village. In the 16th century the river navigation to Exeter was blocked with weirs by some riverbank landowners in order to keep their river levels higher, and the original 1.75 mile Exeter Canal with three locks was completed in 1566 to bypass the weir obstructions. Small vessels could use the canal while the larger vessels had to offload at Topsham. The canal was extended out to Topsham in 1676, then deepened and widened in 1701 (as the first ship canal) allowing sea going vessels to reach Exeter. The ports of both Exeter and Topsham thrived, while Exmouth (under the control of Exeter) was prevented from doing so. Topsham was a major port with regular passages to London, Torquay, and the Channel Isles until the railways arrived in 1842. In 1844 when the canal was finally extended, the entrance lock was two miles downstream from Topsham thus effectively bypassing Topsham, and reducing its trade. When steam took over from sail, combined with a new rail link from Exeter to Exmouth in 1861, trade at Topsham ceased completely. Sea going trade into Exeter ceased in 1970, and the Exeter basin was closed to all vessels in 1996. The canal itself remains open as far as the Exeter Ring road.

A dock was built at Exmouth in 1825, sheltering craft from the strong tidal currents, and Exmouth gradually developed as the major port for the River Exe. Exmouth became a major landing port for herring. With Weymouth it is one of two sheltered ports on the south coast within easy reach of London, and consequently became a major landing place for fish destined for the London markets, especially once the railways reached the West Country. Commercial use of the docks ceased in 1989 and the dock has been made into a marina development. About two dozen fishing vessels operate from the River Exe with most of them based at Exmouth itself or opposite in the shelter of the Dawlish Warren sand spit. The fish quay is in the entrance to the marina dock and several fishing vessels moor up in the marina, especially during the winter months.

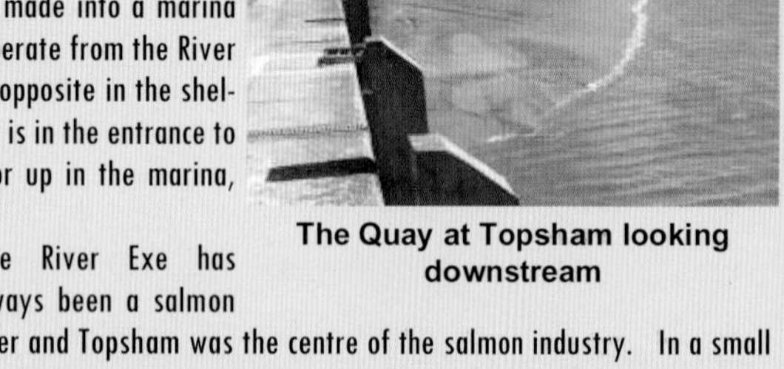

The Quay at Topsham looking downstream

Ex RX76 Lumbering Elephant
(Possibly aptly named!!)

The River Exe has always been a salmon river and Topsham was the centre of the salmon industry. In a small inlet cut into the river bank at Topsham a few small salmon netters, locally registered in Exeter, can be found still operating . The licences are registered with the owner rather than to the boats, so it is possible for several boats to hold the same registration number if they belong to the same owner. There are three boats numbered E15. Mussel dredging takes place just inside the estuary north of Dawlish Warren, and whelk potting is carried out just outside the river estuary. Some fishing boats finish up with a variety of uses (*see left).*

RIVER EXE FISHING VESSELS (Exmouth E & Topsham T)

Ph		Reg	VESSEL NAME	Type	LOA	Reg	Eng	Year	Hull	Nat
					Mtrs	Tons	KW	Built		Build
p	T	E3	(Unnamed)	Salmon Netter	<4.5				F	GBR
p	T	E6	(Unnamed)	Salmon Netter	<4.5				F	GBR
p	T	E15	KIMBERLEY	Salmon Netter	<6				F	GBR
p	T	E15	(Unnamed)	Salmon Netter	<4.5				F	GBR
p	T	E18	(Unnamed)	Salmon Netter	<7				W	GBR
p	T	E19	(Unnamed)	Salmon Netter					W	GBR
p	E	BM249	SARAH JAYNE	Beam Trawl	14.94	23.6	186	1979	30	GBR
p	E	E22	ROANNE	Potter	4.14	0.7	30	1981	F	GBR
p	E	E23	ZOE of LADRAM	Netter/Potter	8.85	6.5	253	2004	F	GBR
p	T	Ex E53	ELSIE	De-registered	<7				W	GBR
p	E	E74	LOUISE	Angler	5.65	1.6	13		F	
p	E	E87	PROVIDER	Trawler	10.00	7.5	145	1990	S	GBR
p	T	E92	ESME	Salmon Netter	4.26	0.8	4	1989	F	GBR
p	E	E123	EMILY J	Trawler/Scalloper	11.93	21.1	221	2004	S	GBR
p	E	E144	RYDS	Netter	4.65	0.8	15	1990	F	GBR
p	E	E163	STRIKER	Tender	5.10	1.1	18	1990	F	GBR
p	E	Ex E183	STELLA MARIS	De-registered	11.70	21.9	220	1988	F	GBR
p	E	E449	LUCY M	Netter	5.10	1.1	19	1989	F	GBR
p	E	E451	TREBLE TTT	Potter	7.10	3.6	15	1976	W	GBR
p	E	E455	VOLUNTEER	Netter	4.78	1.1	22	1991	F	GBR
p	E	Ex E461	SOMEDAY SOON	De-registered	5.25	0.3	45	1980	F	GBR
p	E	Ex E476	MARGH AN MOR	De-registered	6.00	1.7	14	1979	F	GBR
p	E	E495	SOPHIE OF LADRAM	Trawler	14.97	27.5	252	1999	F	GBR
p	E	E508	BECCI OF LADRAM	Netter/Potter	9.79	5.5	298	2001	F	GBR
p	E	E516	ALIBI	Mussel Dredger	9.99	3.1	75	1991	A	FRA
p	E	E520	MIA B	Whelker	9.88	6.2	148	2005	F	GBR
p	E	E521	ROWELLA of LADRAM	Whelker	11.85	11.5	150	1978	W	GBR
p	E	E530	SELINA JOY	Potter	10.0	8	118	1999	F	GBR
p	E	E533	PROSPERITY	Potter	8.4	5	93	1999	F	GBR
p	E	E534	ATTITUDE	Netter/Potter	9.0	6	85	1985	S	GBR
p	E	E535	BETTY-G (Ex NN716)	Trawler/Scalloper	9.9	14	119	2000	S	GBR
p	E	Ex FY473	BEKIDIL	De-registered	<6				F	GBR
p	E	KY115	FLOURISH	Trawler/Scalloper	9.7	21	216	1991	S	GBR
p	E	KY467	THREE BOYS	Trawler	9.9	13	120	1997	S	GBR
p	E	LI79	SANDELLA	Potter	7.32	1.6	37	1988	F	GBR
p	E	OB2	PROSPECT	Scalloper	9.98	10.0	171	1999	S	GBR
p	E	PW443	STRIKE	Netter	5.10	1.0	21	1997	F	GBR
p	E	SM241	TWO BROTHERS	Trawler/Scalloper	11.49	11.6	144	1987	S	GBR
p	E	SM271	ANGELINA	Trawler/Scalloper	13.99	19.4	134	1988	W	
p	E	SM690	SEA GEM	Netter	5.08	1.3	15	1992	F	GBR
p	E	Ex YH5	GOLDEN HARVEST	De-registered	7.05	1.9	41	1992	F	GBR

E3 (Unnamed) - 02/01/2006

E6 (Unnamed) - 18/02/2006

E15 (Unnamed) - 18/02/2006

E15 Kimberley - 02/01/2005

E18 (Unnamed) - 18/02/2006

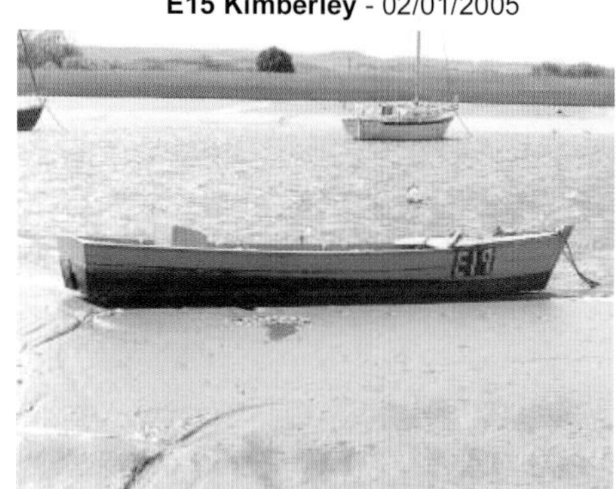

E19 (Unnamed) - 06/05/2005

BM249 Sarah Jayne - 14/02/2005

E22 Roanne - 10/04/2004

E23 Zoe of Ladram - 02/01/2006

Ex E53 Elsie - 18/02/2006

E74 Louise - 18/02/2006

E87 Provider - 02/01/2005

E92 Esme - 18/02/2006

E123 Emily J - 06/05/2005

E144 Ryds - 06/05/2005

E163 Striker - 10/04/2004

Ex E183 Stella Maris - 17/06/2004

E449 Lucy M - 10/04/2004

E451 Treble TTT - /2004

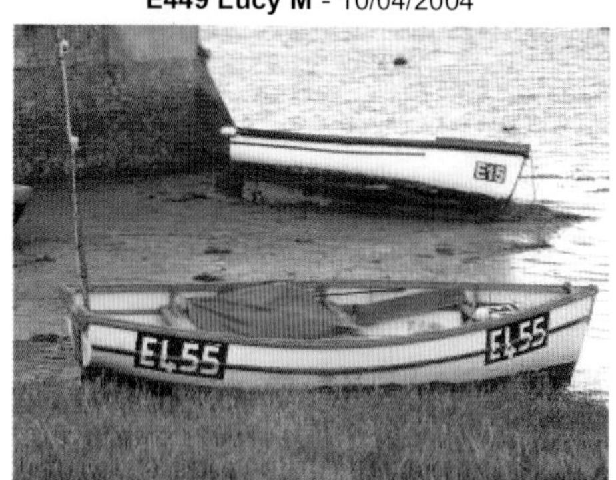

E455 Volunteer - 19/05/2005

Ex E461 Someday Soon - 03/03/2006

Ex E476 Margh An Mor - 10/04/2005

E508 Becci of Ladram - 22/07/2005

E516 Alibi - 14/01/2006

E520 Mia B - 18/02/2006

E521 Rowella of Ladram - 20/02/2006

E530 Selina Joy - 22/07/2005

E533 Prosperity - 10/04/2004

E534 Attitude- 10/04/2005

E535 Betsy-G - 10/04/2005

Ex FY473 Bekidil- 18/02/2005

KY115 Flourish - 18/02/2006

KY467 Three Boys - 23/10/2005

LI79 Sandella - 02/01/2006

OB2 Prospect - 18/02/2006

PW443 Strike - 14/02/2005

SM241 Two Brothers II - 18/02/2006

SM271 Angelina - 04/07/2005

SM690 Sea Gem - 06/05/2005

Ex YH5 Golden Harvest - 02/01/2005

TEIGNMOUTH

River Teign - *Fish Quay on extreme right*

Mouth of the River Teign, *looking North*

The River Teign has been a major fishing haven since the 13th century. Teignmouth itself has the claim of being the last place in England at which a brief invasion by foreign troops actually succeeded, in 1690 by the French. The river has also been an important export base for Dartmoor ball clay and granite stone. The wooden road bridge was built in 1827, and rebuilt in 1838, with a narrow bascule opening which prevented shipping over 300 tons moving up river. The bridge is now fixed. Barges however, used to go up to the short Stover Canal and the even shorter Hackney Canal, both near Newton Abbot, to collect china clay and granite stone. (The stone for London Bridge was shipped from here.) The Stover Canal was just under 2 miles long and built in the 1790s, while the Hackney Canal was only 5/8th mile long and opened in 1843. They both remained open until the 1930s. Despite the dangerous shifting sand-bar off the entrance, which has claimed many a vessel, Teignmouth is a thriving commercial port and shipping still uses the quay, which was originally built in 1830 and later extended in 1900. The town also supports about 24 fishing boats of all kinds, operating from the mouth of the River. Although strongly tidal it lies in the lee of the prevailing SWly winds and boats can get alongside at, or close to, low water. Most of the boats bear the 'TH' (Teignmouth) registration. The fish quay is positioned on the north bank just downstream from the commercial quays. Since it is quite small, the boats are moored all around the waters inside the narrow river entrance but the larger vessels usually moor opposite the commercial quays, just below the bridge. Most of the catches go to Brixham fish market but some are taken by road as far away as Poole.

TEIGNMOUTH FISHING VESSELS

Photo	Reg	NAME	TYPE	LOA Mtrs	REG Tons	Eng KW	Year Build	Hull	Nat Build
p	BM76	HELL-OF-A-DEAR	Out of Area	6.6	3.3	57	1994	F	GBR
p	BM273	THREE SISTERS	Netter/Potter	7.1	1.9	10	1968	W	GBR
p	BM499	ATLANTIS II	Potter	10.0	2.7	145	1997	F	GBR
p	DH300	JODIE ANN	Netter/Potter	6.7	1.6	47	1992	F	GBR
p	E484	ST NICHOLAS II	Trawler	6.1	1.5	34	1994	F	GBR
p	FH672	KAISA MARI	Angler	5.1	1.3	21	1998	F	GBR
p	ExFY773	CARA MOR	De-registered	5.6	1.9	15	1994	F	GBR
p	J612	LA VAGABONDE	Potter	17.7	35.0	335	1969	W	FRA
p	PH101	SNOWDROP	Netter	5.7	1.6	29	1989	F	GBR
p	PH326	MOBY DICK	Trawler/Netter	9.2	9.7	95	1976	W	FRA
p	Ex PW11	EMMA KATE	De-registered	8.8	5.6	59	1982	W	GBR
p	PZ1189	JESSICA IONE	Netter	6.4	2.4	32	1999	F	GBR
p	RX369	LISANA (Ex Bethan Louise)	Potter	7.2	5.2	26	1991	F	GBR

TEIGNMOUTH

p	SC84	FAITH	Netter	6.2	2.3	22	1991	F	GBR
p	Ex SE1	SUMMERWINE	De-registered	7.1					
p	TH19	HENRY	Netter	5.5	1.6	15	1996	F	GBR
p	TH20	MARGARET	Netter	5.5	1.4	10	1966	W	GBR
p	TH37	ALICE	Netter/Potter	5.8		20	1956	W	GBR
p	Ex TH64	HOPKINS 1	De-registered	4.9	1.2	8	1982	W	GBR
p	Ex TH71	POLARLYS	De-registered	5.0	1.3	7	0	W	GBR
	TH82	MOIRA F		4.14	0.36	3	1998	F	GBR
p	TH86	SAMMY B	Netter	4.7	0.9	11	1978	F	GBR
p	Ex TH115	SANTOY	De-registered	4.9	0.8	11		F	GBR
p	TH117	GIRL RONA	Scalloper/Netter	15.1	24.5	216	1980	S	GBR
p	TH119	THREE FEVERS	Netter	7.0	4.3	4	1970	F	GBR
p	TH121	DIVERSE	Potter	5.0	1.0	18	1987	F	GBR
p	TH155	DEEPCORE	Netter/Potter	5.7	1.3	45	1988	F	GBR
p	TH165	BOY KARL	Netter	5.7	1.4	37	1990	F	GBR
p	TH417	VALKYRIE	Potter	5.6	1.9	13	1998	F	GBR
p	TH422	SILVER FOX	Angler	8.1	3.6	164	2001	F	POL
p	TH424	KAY-LARIE (Ex SU414)	Netter	6.6	3.5	41	1978	F	GBR
p	WH696	ETOILE DES ONDES	Potter	16.3	31.4	184	1957	W	FRA

Ex BM76 Hell-of-a-Dear - 18/01/2005

BM273 Three Sisters - 10/04/2005

BM499 Atlantis II - 10/02/2006

DH300 Jodie Ann - 10/02/2006

E484 St Nicholas II - 20/08/2006

FH672 Kaisa Mari - 20/08/2006

Ex FY773 Cara Mor - 20/08/2006

J612 La Vagabonde des Mers - 18/01/2005

PH101 Snowdrop - 10/02/2006

PH326 Moby Dick - 06/05/2005

Ex PW11 Emma Kate - 10/02/2006

PZ1189 Jessica Ione - 29/03/2005

RX369 Lisana - 18/01/2005

SC84 Faith– 29/03/2005

Ex SE1 Summerwine - 10/02/2006

TH19 Henry - 10/02/2006

TH20 Margaret - 20/08/2004

TH37 Alice – 20/08/2004

Ex TH64 Hopkins I - 20/08/2004

Ex TH71 Polarlis - 20/08/2004

TEIGNMOUTH

TH86 Sammy B - 10/02/2006

TH115 Santoy - 20/08/2004

TH117 Girl Rona - 10/02/2006

TH119 Three Fevers - 10/02/2006

TH121 Diverse - 10/02/2006

TH155 Deepcore – 20/08/2006

TH165 Boy Karl – 18/01/2005

TH417 Valkyrie - 20/08/2004

TEIGNMOUTH

TH422 Silver Fox - 20/08/2004

TH424 Kay-Larie - 10/02/2006

WH696 Etoile des Ondes - 20/08/2004

56 TORQUAY

Harbour Entrance from the Fish Quay

The Municipal Pontoon

There are three harbours in Tor Bay, namely Torquay, Paignton and Brixham. Before the breakwater at Plymouth was completed in 1841, the Royal Navy preferred using Torbay, along with all its facilities and excellent shelter from the prevailing south westerly winds, in preference to Plymouth Sound. 397 Prisoners who had been captured from the Spanish Armada were kept in Torquay in July 1588 in a Tithe barn in the grounds of Torre Abbey, now labelled the 'Spanish Barn'. Torquay harbour was originally just a small drying out harbour until the outer harbour wall was

The Spanish Barn

constructed in 1860. The port was still very exposed to the South East however until the southern breakwater - Haldon Pier - was extended in 1984. Even now the entrance can still be tricky in a strong SEly wind. The depth in the old drying out harbour is now controlled by a sophisticated moveable dam. There is some fishing activity - potting, netting and lining, by part time fishermen from the original fish quay, situated between the old and newer harbour basins. About eight small fishing craft can be found dotted around the harbour, with several mooring at the municipal jetty in the North West corner of the harbour. Two ten metre trawlers are also based in the port but frequently operate from Brixham. The 'BM' and 'TH' registrations predominate. The large slipways at the north end of the harbour were built to embark troops leaving for D-Day.

The Fish Quay

TORQUAY FISHING VESSEL LIST

Photo	Reg	VESSEL NAME	Type	LOA Mtrs	REG Tons	ENG Kw	Year Built	Hull	Nat Build
p	BM11	LIAM JOHN II	Potter	5.72	1.40	30	1991	F	GBR
p	BM40	BOY PHILLIP	Netter	5.6	1.4	30	1989	F	GBR
p	BM342	OUR WENDY	Liner/Potter	5.0	1.0	15	1987	G	GBR
p	BM482	MARY ANNE	Trawler	11.98	15.2	149	1997	S	GBR
p	BM503	J C K	Potter	5.65	0.96	29	1988	G	GBR
p	IH260	GIRL TRACEY	Netter	5.16	1.07	15	-	F	GBR
p	HL42	ENDEAVOUR	Trawler	9.95	9.94	201	2000	S	GBR
p	LI535	ALK II	Potter	4.9	1.2	11	1980	F	GBR
p	TH74	SALEDA BLANCHE	Liner	5.7	1.5	30	1989	F	GBR
p	TH419	EMALEY	Netter	6.0	1.5	30	0	F	

BM11 Liam John II - 20/08/2006

BM40 Boy Phillip – 20/07/2005

BM342 Our Wendy - 04/07/2005

BM482 Mary Anne - 20/08/2006

BM503 J C K - 20/08/2006

HL42 Endeavour– 13/03/2006

IH260 Girl Tracey - 20/07/2005

LI535 Alk II - 21/06/2004

TH74 Saleda Blanche - 13/03/2006

TH419 Emaley – 04/07/2005

PAIGNTON

The Harbour

Harbour Entrance - Torquay beyond

The first mention of Paignton (then Peynton) as a harbour dates back to 1567, and seine net fishing was well established sometime in the 16th century. The fishermen lived in cottages above the fish cellars on the north side of the harbour. Prior to construction of the harbour and quays in 1839, the harbour consisted merely of a short pier. It gained fame (or notoriety) in 1935 as being the only harbour to have a female harbour master!! It is now a drying out harbour, much as was the original Torquay harbour, and along with many pleasure craft a few small potters can now be found operating from it.

PAIGNTON FISHING VESSEL LIST

Photo	Reg	VESSEL NAME	Type	LOA Mtrs	REG Tons	ENG Kw	Year Built	Hull	Nat Build
p	Ex BM98	LITTLE BOY BLUE	De-registered	4.30	0.58	6	1992	W	GBR
p	BM98	LITTLE BOY BLUE	Potter	4.85	0.80	11	1998	F	GBR
p	BM129	SHONALEE	Potter	5.6	1.8	9	1978	F	GBR
p	BM513	SILVER SPRAY	Potter	5.63	1.91	13	1985	G	GBR
p	Ex CA44	INNISFREE	De-registered	6.4	2.4	26	1982	F	GBR
p	R39	CLAIRE LOUISE	Potter	8.6	6.7	53	1985	F	GBR
p	TH135	ROCK HOPPER	Potter	4.9	1.1	7	1988	F	GBR

Ex BM98 Little Boy Blue - 21/06/2004

BM98 Little Boy Blue - 24/07/2006

BM129 Shonalee - 29/03/2005

BM513 Silver Spray - 20/08/2004

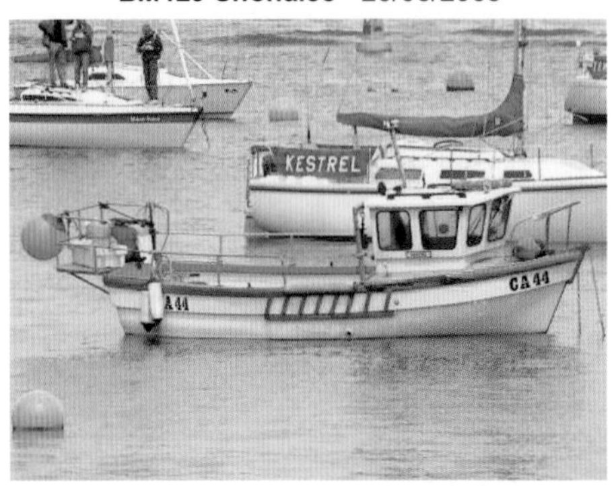

Ex CA44 Innisfree - 02/05/2004

R39 Clare Louise - 20/07/2005

TH135 Rock Hopper - 29/03/2005

BRIXHAM

The Breakwater and Yacht Marina

Brixham Fish Harbour looking North West

Brixham as a fishing port was mentioned in the Doomsday Book and in 1500 was recorded as having a major pilchard industry. History records that William of Orange passed through Brixham in 1688, and was the last successful invader of England, becoming its King, and that the less successful Napoleon Bonaparte was brought in as a prisoner from the wars against the French in 1815. By 1850 it supported the largest fishing fleet in England, with some 200 vessels, mainly trawlers. Brixham was renowned for the fast, seaworthy Trawlers which with their large powerful sail area were capable of nearly 12 knots. There are still a few of them operating from the port, albeit for pleasure (see page xi). The design of these powerful boats was subsequently used to develop the trawler fleets on the East Coast. The short broad gauge railway branch line to join up with the main rail network boosted the port's importance, and at the start of the 20th century there were roughly 300 trawlers, about 150 of them between 30 and 40 tons, and 75 smaller up to 25 tons. The major decrease came at the end of WW1due to competition from the North East fishing fleets, and by 1930 there were as few as seven major fishing vessels at Brixham. Only since the 1960s has the industry started to recover, and there is now a large modern trawler fleet operating from Brixham to the seas all round Britain. In 1986 Brixham was the fourth largest port in the UK for fish landings, and in 2004 just took over from Newlyn as the leading port in the South West. A total of some 90 fishing vessels of all types operate from the port, about half of which are the larger deep sea boats. A gradual change is taking place however from the large 'Beamers' to smaller vessels of less than 15metres length, which are cheaper to operate with less crew and smaller fuel demands. The fuel price for a one week trip for a large beamer has gone up from £2,000 to £8,000 in less than a year. About 50 boats bear the 'BM' (Brixham) registration. The port provides superb sheltered access, with its long breakwater providing shelter from the North East, and that provided by Tor Bay to the North and Berry Head to the South. While the inner harbour dries out, most of the commercial fish harbour is accessible at all ranges of tide. The 3000ft outer breakwater was started in 1843, but lack of money meant it was built in stages and only finally completed in 1916. The disused oil jetty at the seaward end of the breakwater was built in 1920, originally to supply steam ships with heavy duty oil from storage tanks in the Old Quarry at the landward end. In 1934 it was used to store a surplus of Whale Oil, and in 1936 its use changed for the storage of aviation fuel (then petrol) along with new huge underground storage tanks on Berry Head. The petrol came in by sea, and out via the Brixham railway branch line. It was again used for storage of fuel oil for 10 years following the Suez crisis until North Sea Oil was discovered. It then reverted to being used for ship bunkering until 1988 when its use ceased. The slipway at the shore end

The Fish Harbour looking South East

Original Open Fish Market by the Inner Harbour

King William's Fish Quay

of the breakwater is a hangover from WW2, when Brixham was a major departure point for the D-Day landings. The original fish quay was just a short pier extending westwards. The present King Williams Fish Quay (*named after William of Orange*) extending northwards, was completed in 1971 and considerably improved in 1985. Further developments are planned on the shoreline to the north. There are about 25 companies employed in processing and packing the fish, and the fish industry provides about 2500 jobs. An ice plant was opened in Brixham in 1860 using ice carved from frozen lakes in Norway, wrapped in straw, and brought in by fast brig. A manufacturing plant to make ice was then built in 1900 on King's Quay on the south side of the harbour. It was powered initially by steam and later by oil. It went out of use in 1970 and was replaced only in 1987 when the present modern plant was built on King William's Quay. Most of the larger vessels use the main fish harbour but several moor up inside the breakwater north of the yacht Marina while some of their tenders- registered boats in their own right - can be found in the marina itself. The smaller craft will usually be found in the inner harbour, though that is sometimes also used by the larger craft when maintenance is required and they can dry out against the

BRIXHAM FISHING VESSELS

Photo	Reg	Vessels Name	Type	LOA Mtrs	Reg Tons	Eng Kw	Year	Hull	NAT Build
p	BCK160	BLUE ANGEL	Beam Trawler	33.4	205.0	661	1981	S	BEL
p	BD257	MALLAGAR	Trawler	9.8	9.7	134	1995	F	GBR
p	BH9	VALHALLA	Trawler	18.15	85	187	1985	W	GBR
p	BM1	GUYONA	Trawler	13.1	34.2	116	1982	S	GBR
p	BM2	HANNAH D	Netter	10.0	7.1	126	1978	F	GBR
p	BM4	SEAHUNTER	Trawler/Scalloper	12.2	39.9	184	1989	S	GBR
p	BM5	DEE-J (Ex ML113 Stormchild)	Trawler (Ex Polperro)	10.0	7.1	120	1978	F	GBR
p	BM6	REEL ONE	Tender	<6				F	GBR
p	BM7	LADY MAUREEN (Ex J276)	Beam Trawler	34.15	205.0	920	1973	S	NLD
p	BM10	EMELIA M ETHEL(ExPW14)	Beam Trawler	23.00	125.0	221	1991	S	NLD
p	BM12	SYDO	Trawler	13.8	22.8	126	1954	W	NOR
p	BM23	CARHELMAR	Beam Trawler	23.8	128.0	220	1989	S	NLD
p	BM24	PEACE AND PLENTY III	Trawler	11.7	22.9	119	1983	S	GBR
p	BM27	OUR MIRANDA	Beam Trawler	25.3	142.0	552	1982	S	NLD
p	BM28	ANGEL EMIEL	Beam Trawler	23.1	125.0	219	1990	S	POL
p	ExBM28	PROVIDENT	Brixham Trawler	24.0	84.0		1924	W	GBR
p	BM30	SARA LENA	Out of Area	18.2	82.0	220	1990	S	NLD
p	BM44	NIPPER	Potter	5.9	1.9	16	1986	F	GBR
p	BM46	TT to SARAH JAYNE BM249	Tender	5.9	1.9	29	1986	W	GBR
p	BM51	HARM JOHANNES	Beam Trawler	25.4	83.0	221	1954	S	NLD
p	BM55	KRYST-LE-KAY	Netter	9.3	7.3	95		W	FRA
p	BM66	MAR ROSE	Potter	8.00	5.44	115	1974	W	FRA
p	BM67	GINA LOUISE	Trawler	12.5	16.8	134	1977	W	FRA
p	Ex BM76	VIGILANCE	Brixham Trawler	22.0	95.0		1926	W	GBR
p	BM77	JACOBA	Beam Trawler	27.0	108.0	537	1968	S	NLD

BRIXHAM

p	BM79	ADELA	Trawler	9.2	8.7	134	1981	W	
p	Ex BM87	LES MERCENAIRES	SANK Nov 2005	10.0	8.8	112	1972	W	FRA
p	BM102	SCORPION LASS	Potter	6.1	1.8	23	1980	F	GBR
	BM107	SISTER MC B		6.7	3.1	49	1982	F	GBR
p	BM115	MY MIKAELA	Trawler	9.98	9.4	90	1989	F	GBR
p	BM127	HARVESTER (Ex E496)	Trawler/Scalloper	15.2	27.6	266	1999	S	GBR
p	BM128	LADY LOU	Beam Trawler	28.15	167.0	706	1968	S	NLD
p	BM140	GEESKE	Scalloper	30.40	171.0	588	1971	S	NLD
p	BM147	MALKERRY	Trawler	13.72	26.0	216	1985	S	GBR
p	BM150	OUR MARIA	Netter	10.00	16.1	127	1987	F	GBR
p	BM165	SERENA	Trawler/Scalloper	9.98	16.16	216	1998	S	GBR
p	BM166	LERINA	Trawler	9.85	15.1	120	1997	S	GBR
p	BM169	THREE SONS (ExMarilyn Jayne)	Beam Trawler	26.15	105.0	373	1967	S	NLD
p	BM172	OUR JOHANNA	Beam Trawler	26.20	153.0	669	1971	S	NLD
p	BM176	EBONNIE	Crabber	14.95	69.5	223	2005	S	GBR
p	BM177	LA CREOLE	Potter	12.72	17.7	107	1967	W	FRA
p	BM181	SASHA EMIEL	Beam Trawler	33.86	242.0	749	1980	S	NLD
p	BM188	LLOYD TYLER (Ex BCK40)	Beam Trawler	26.20	151.0	507	1970	S	NLD
p	BM190	MARINA	Trawler	11.40	21.2	221	1989	S	GBR
p	BM192	RACHEL LOUISE	Trawler	8.6	9.5	120	1997	S	GBR
p	Ex BM202	(ONZE) LIQUENDA	De-registered	26.39	86.0	336	1956	S	NLD
p	BM208	JACOMINA	Beam Trawler	25.15	86.0	475	1966	S	NLD
p	BM218	HARINGVLIET	Beam Trawler	29.75	127.0	705	1968	S	NLD
p	BM219	TRITON	Angler	6.30	2.1	60	1990	F	GBR
p	BM222	SEA OTTER (Ex BM19 & DS7)	Trawler/Scalloper	15.24	38.0	221	1984	S	GBR
p	ExBM222	MOURNE LASS	Motor Yacht	15.82	33.9	128	1947	W	GBR
p	BM234	DE VROUW MARIE	Beam Trawler	30.40	188.0	597	1972	S	NLD
p	BM241	MAGDALENA	Beam Trawler	29.90	155.0	596	1964	S	NLD
p	Ex BM247	ARCOMINE	De-registered	30.73	173.0	401	1963	S	NLD
p	BM248	JACKY J	Potter	8.30	2.8	134	1979	F	GBR
p	BM258	HELEN CLAIRE	Potter	14.39	33.8	149	1959	W	GBR
p	BM264	OUR ZOE ANNE	Beam Trawler	29.85	153.0	563	1968	S	NLD
p	BM265	JOANNA C	Trawler/Scalloper	14.81	28.6	205	1980	S	GBR
p	Ex BM278	ONDARRUMAN	De-registered	33.80	184.0	560	1965	S	ESP
p	BM282	CATEAR	Beam Trawler	28.95	150.0	671	1973	S	NLD
p	BM362	VAN DIJCK	Scalloper	33.53	203.0	746	1974	S	BEL
p	Ex BM474	MYSTERE	De-registered	5.50	1.5	30	1990	F	GBR
p	BM478	DANIELLE	Scalloper	31.99	226.0	634	1973	S	NLD
p	BM479	LISA K	Trawler	9.82	7.2	40	1973	W	FRA
	BM482	MARY ANNE	Trawler	11.98	15.2	149	1997	S	GBR
p	BM484	CONSTANT FRIEND	Trawler/Scalloper	15.20	28.7	220	1998	S	GBR
p	Ex BM485	CHRISTINIE	De-registered	9.87	10.5	112	1992	S	GBR

BRIXHAM

p	BM488	THANKFUL	Netter	7.62	3.3	31	1974	F	UNK
p	BM491	NICOLA JAYNE	Potter	5.00	0.9	35	1997	G	GBR
	BM498	EMERALD	Trawler	9.95	6.5	94	1961	W	GBR
p	BM508	JOSE JACQUELINE	Fish Farm	11.50		81	1977	S	GBR
p	BM510	ANGUS ROSE (Ex BM165)	Scalloper	24.00	89.0	221	1962	S	NLD
p	BM516	TWO BROTHERS	Trawler	9.99	6.9	93	1979	S	GBR
p	BM517	KASEY MARIE (Ex BRD493)	Scalloper	13.40	21.5	104	1983	S	GBR
p	BM522	THON-B	Fish Farm					S	
p	BM2000	LADY T EMIEL	Beam Trawler	32.80	239.0	747	1985	S	NLD
p	BS472	ELISE (Ex Gwenfaen)	Trawler	9.90	6.5	150	2002	F	GBR
p	ExBW40	HAZY DAWN	De-registered	6.70					
p	Ex DH10	(Unknown)	De-registered						
p	DH46	INDEPENDENT	Potter	10.59	9.4	94	1973	W	FRA
p	E6	EVELYN	Out of Area	7.90	2.7	67	2001	F	GBR
p	E444	GIRL DEBRA	Trawler/Scalloper	14.98	38.2	221	2000	S	GBR
p	E456	LITTLE GEM	Tender to BM249	4.9	1.4	26	1986	F	GBR
p	E495	AMY R (Ex Sophie of Ladram)	Trawler/Scalloper	14.97	27.5	252	1999	S	GBR
p	FD100	CHRISTINA	Beam Trawler	28.00	161.0	448	1973	S	NLD
p	ExFD407	KATIE CLAIRE (ExTwinB)	Now PZ87 Newlyn	13.45	21.6	108	1996	S	GBR
p	FH253	PETITE ANGELA	Trawler	10.00	9.2	89	1972	W	FRA
p	FH258	KENDORE (Ex Falmouth)	Trawler	9.91	12.0	164	1978	F	GBR
p	FH496	CRAGGAN	Potter	7.80	5.3	80	1979	F	GBR
p	FR927	PROPITIOUS	Trawler	9.99	13.0	116	2000		GBR
p	HL1054	SUVERA	Potter	9.80	12.0	101	1992	F	GBR
p	IH23	OUR STEPH	Trawler	9.20	6.5	90	1989	F	GBR
p	Ex J347	GRIETJE (Ex Plymouth)	De-registered	31.73	73.8	368	1964	S	NLD
p	LT22	SOPHIE DAWN	Out of Area	9.98	8.9	97	1989	F	GBR
p	Ex LT266	SENEX FIDELIS	De-registered	25.45	99.2	221	1967	S	NLD
p	LT535	KORENBLOEM	Beam Trawler	27.53	123.0	596	1968	S	OTH
p	M1141	LUCY	Potter	5.60	1.3	14	1982	F	GBR
p	NN138	ALEYNA	Trawler/Scalloper	13.96	20.3	176	1989	S	GBR
p	NN257	CARINA	Trawler/Scalloper	13.95	21.3	187	1991	S	GBR
p	OB254	VIRGO	Trawler/Sclloper	15.15	27.8	134	1968	W	GBR
p	OB438	FEUSGAN	Potter	7.65	3.8	111	1989	F	GBR
p	OB454	KELLY MARENA II	Trawler	9.99	13.1	112	1998	S	GBR
p	PE487	LIBRA LASS	Netter/Potter	7.20	2.6	63	1989	F	GBR
p	ExPH5546	ALBATROSS	De-registered	8.90	3.4	45	1960	W	GBR
p	PH5585	NEW DAWN (Ex GU360)	Scalloper	11.36	13.8	90	1965	W	FRA
p	PW160	FIONA MARY	Netter	9.99	9.2	84	1972	W	FRA
p	PW201	LA CONQUETE	Trawler	9.85	7.9	126	1982	W	GBR
p	R84	BUMBLE B	Potter	5.85	0.7	29	1989	F	GBR

BRIXHAM

p	SE20	LITTLE EMIEL	Potter	6.20	2.3	35	0	W	UNK
p	SE29	SUNSEEKER II	Potter	6.93	3.5	24	1981	W	GBR
p	SE40	KATRINA	Scalloper	9.98	9.2	112	1999	S	GBR
p	ExSH297	SHANICE PATRICIA (Ex BM489)	De-registered	9.96	11.44	127	1998	S	GBR
p	TH257	GERRY ANN C	Trawler/Scalloper	15.24	24.5	213	1975	S	GBR
p	WH584	KALUGER	Trawler	9.85	16.8	172	91	S	GBR

BCK160 Blue Angel - 29/04/2005

BD257 Mallagar - 21/07/2006

BH9 Valhalla - 01/04/2006

BM1 Guyona - 07/11/2004

BM2 Hannah D - 04/02/2006

BM4 Seahunter - 04/02/2006

BM5 Dee-J - 04/02/2006

BM6 Reel One - 21/07/2006

BM7 Lady Maureen - 28/04/2005

BM10 Emelia M Ethel - 21/07/2006 (DL)

BM12 Sydo - 21/07/2006

BM23 Carhelmar - 30/08/2006

BM24 Peace & Plenty III - 01/02/2006

BM27 Our Miranda - 30/08/2006

BM28 Angel Emiel - 01/02/2006

Ex BM28 Provident - 17 /05/2006

BM30 Sara Lena - 14/06/2005

BM44 Nipper - 02/05/2004

BM46 TT to Sarah Jane (BM249) - 01/02/2006

BM51 Harm Johannes - 17/06/2006 (DL)

BM55 Kryst Le Kay – 20/08/2006

BM66 Mar Rose– 01/02/2006

BM67 Gina Louise- 01/02/2006

Ex BM76 Vigilance - 31/07/2004

BM77 Jacoba - 29/04/2005

BM79 Adela - 21/07/2006

Ex BM87 Les Mercenaires - 02/05/2004

BM102 Scorpion Lass - 24/07/2006

BM115 My Mikaela - 21/07/2006

BM127 Harvester - 04/02/2006

BM128 Lady Lou - 13/03/2006

BM140 Geeske - 17/06/2006

BM147 Malkerry - 29/04/2005

BM150 Our Maria - 01/02/2006

BM165 Serena - 28/02/2005

BM166 Lerina - 21/07/2006

BM169 Three Sons - 31/08/2004

BM172 Our Joanna - 09/04/2006

BM176 Ebonnie - 01/02/2006

BM177 La Creole - 01/04/2006

BM181 Sasha Emiel - 30/06/2006

BM188 Lloyd Tyler - 28/04/2005

BM190 Marina - 07/11/2004

BM192 Rachel Louise - 16/06/2006 (DL)

Ex BM202 Onze Liquenda - 20/05/2004

BM208 Jacomina - 01/04/2006

BM218 Haringvliet - 13/03/2006

BM219 Triton - 14/02/2006

BM222 Sea Otter - 01/02/2006

Ex BM222 Mourne Lass - 04/07/2005

BM234 De Vrouw Marie - 02/05/2004

BM241 Magdelena - 13/03/2006

Ex BM247 Arcomine - 02/05/2004

BM248 Jack J - 31/07/2004

BM258 Helen Claire - 01/04/2006

BM264 Our Zoe Anne - 13/03/2006

BM265 Joanna C - 29/04/2005

Ex BM278 Ondarruman - 22/11/2003

BM282 Catear - 08/11/2004

BM362 Van Dijck - 02/05/2004

BM474 Mystere - 24/07/2006

BM478 Danielle - 02/05/2004

BM479 Lisa K - 01/04/2006

BM484 Constant Friend - 04/02/2006

BM485 Christinie - 10/09/2003

BM488 Thankful - 02/05/2004

BM491 Nicola Jayne - 02/05/2004

BM508 Jose Jacqueline - 24/07/2006

BM510 Angus Rose - 04/07/2005

BM516 Two Brothers - 24/07/2006

BM517 Kasey Marie - 01/04/2006

BM522 Thon B - 20/08/2006

BM2000 Lady T Emiel - 10/09/2003

BS472 Elise - 21/07/2006

Ex BW40 Hazy Dawn - 31/07/2004

Ex DH10 (Unknown) - 31/07/2004

DH46 Independent - 13/03/2006

E6 Evelyn - 02/05/2004

E444 Girl Debra - 22/02/2005

E456 Little Gem - 01/02/2006

E495 Amy R - 10/09/2003

FD100 Christina - 04/02/2006

Ex FD407 Twin B - 29/08/2003

FH253 Petite Angela - 01/04/2006

FH258 Kendore - 24/07/2006

FH496 Craggan - 21/07/2006

FR927 Propitious - 01/04/2006

HL1054 Suvera - 04/07/2005

IH23 Our Steph - 31/07/2004

Ex J347 Grietje - 30/06/2003

LT22 Sophie Dawn - 02/05/2004

Ex LT266 Senex Fidelis - 31/07/2005

LT535 Korenbloom - 29/04/2005

M1141 Lucy - 04/02/2006

BRIXHAM

NN138 Aleyna - 21/07/2006

NN257 Carina - 08/07/2005

OB254 Virgo - 10/04/2006

OB438 Feusgan - 20/08/2006

OB454 Kelly Marena II - 24/07/2006

PE487 Libra Lass - 01/02/2005

Ex PH5546 Albatross - 02/05/2004

PH5585 New Dawn - 01/02/2006

PW160 Fiona Mary– 13/03/2006

PW201 La Conquete - 01/04/2006

R84 Bumble B - 13/03/2006

SE20 Little Emiel - 01/02/2006

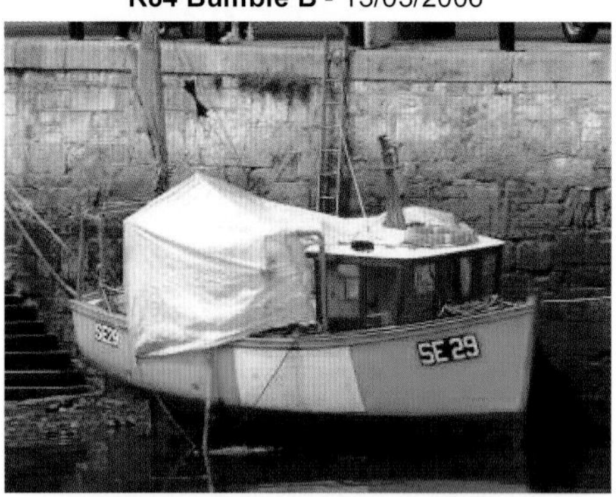

SE29 Sunseeker II - 28/04/2005

SE40 Katrina - 04/06/2004

Ex SH297 Shanice Patricia - 04/07/2005

TH257 Gerry Ann C - 01/04/2006

BRIXHAM

WH584 Kaluger– 13/03/2006

The Inner harbour

Feeding Time!

Lord as I stand on the rolling deck
To view the restless sea
With its expanse of darkened sky,
You seem so far from me.
Intrepid youth should feel no fear,
But I have a load of care
For the safety of our ship and men.
Lord hear my earnest prayer:
That I be true to every task;
May no fault lie with me.
Whatever danger may arise,
As we sail the raging sea.
May I be calm and know that you
Can still the wind and wave,
And be assured in prefect trust
That you have the power to save.
When moon sheds beams from starlit sky,
I feel near to you again'
For the same moon shines on my loved ones too,
And thank you Lord ...Amen (Anon.)

59 DARTMOUTH (KINGSWEAR)

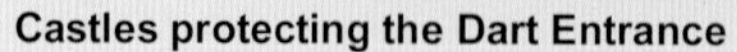

Castles protecting the Dart Entrance

Fish Pontoon Outboard of Kingswear Yacht Marina

Dartmouth was originally founded on the two fishing hamlets of Clifton and Hardness, names which have now passed into history. It therefore has a long fishing history, but it also has a maritime record as a commercial and naval port going back 1000 years. In the late 12th century several fleets sailed from here for 'The Crusades', and in Tudor times it was the most heavily defended port on the South Coast. The two castles at the entrance dating back to 1481 had a chain stretched between them to deter intruders. The Pilgrim Fathers also set off from here after extensive repairs, but were forced to divert into Plymouth for further repairs. During WW2 it was a base for the Free French clandestine visits to France, and Dartmouth provided many small vessels for the Dunkirk evacuation. Finally over 400 vessels and half a million American servicemen left Dartmouth for the D-day landings. Dartmouth has been home to Royal Naval Officer Training since 1863, and the Britannia Royal Naval College which was built in 1905 makes an imposing sight overlooking the river. It is impressive to see the occasional warship passing through the narrow entrance. The entrance to the River Dart is surprisingly well hidden by the high ground surrounding it, but inside is a sheltered deep water harbour with Kingswear on the North side faced by Dartmouth opposite. A combination of wind swirling off the high ground in the entrance and fast running tides can make tricky sea conditions at times. The river is still navigable to Totnes, which was a major port in the Middle Ages, but there is little fishing activity above Dartmouth other than some salmon fishing off Stoke Gabriel. The main fish quay is on the Kingswear side of the river by the railway station. Dartmouth's GWR station (*now a café*) was unique in that its only access to a railway line was via the ferry across to the Kingswear station. About 30 vessels, mainly potters, operate from the port, about seven of which are10m length or greater, and most of them carry the Dartmouth (DH) registration. Several boats moor up on the island pontoon off Kingswear Marina, but fishing vessels can be found moored on both sides of the river. Dartmouth and Salcombe together with Beesands have the largest crab fishery in the UK with spider crabs being exported mainly to France with the brown crabs and lobsters for local consumption.

Looking upstream from Kingswear
Britannia College opposite on the left

The Fish Pontoon

DARTMOUTH FISHING VESSELS

Photo	Reg	VESSEL NAME	Type	LOA Mtrs	Reg Tons	Eng Kw	Year Built	Hull	Nat Build
p	Ex BL31	MISCHIEF	De-registered	4.8	1.5	26	1988	F	GBR
p	DH1	NICKY V	Potter	9.8	6.2	184	1983	F	GBR
p	DH5	WILLIAM HENRY II	Potter	22.5	185.0	362	1989	S	NLD
p	DH8	MAYFLY	Netter	7.3	2.4	37	2004	F	GBR
p	DH17	EXCEL	Potter	15.2	24.5	138	1971	W	GBR
p	DH20	MAGNUM	Potter	11.3	11.2	97	1979	F	GBR
	DH26	FELICITY		4.4	0.9	30	1985	F	GBR
	DH58	SALTPETER		3.1	0.4	4	1985	F	GBR
p	DH60	MAGGIE-MARIE	Trawler	9.3	7.6	98	1976	F	GBR
p	DH63	SKERRY BELLE	Potter	11.5	10.5	63	1974	W	GBR
	DH71	Crusader of Kingswear	Potter	16.9	44.2	171	1976	W	GBR
p	DH76	HEATSEEKER	Potter	9.9	6.7	239	1989	F	GBR
	DH79	TT TO HEATSEEKER		3.5	0.3	11	1982	F	FRA
p	DH88	REJOICE	Potter	6.2	2.9	21	1989	G	GBR
p	DH89	BOBOLINK	Angler	4.7	0.9	52	1992	F	USA
p	DH97	FULL MONTY	Angler	7.8	3.0	164	1997	G	GBR
p	DH99	SUPERB-US	Trawler/Potter	13.6	18.6	82	1964	W	GBR
p	DH119	NORTHERN CLIPPER	Potter	13.0	20.2	112	1971	W	FRA
p	DH133	DAMSEL FLY	Potter	9.3	4.4	56	1980	F	GBR
p	DH135	OUR PAMMY	Potter	8.5	8.1	50	1974	F	GBR
p	DH141	BRITANNIA of BEESANDS	Crabber	9.8	6.4	104	2004	F	GBR
	DH145	XAVIER		4.8	0.9	5	1979	F	GBR
p	DH149	NEWBROOK	Potter	14.3	15.8	95	1960	W	GBR
p	DH179	SEA SOLDIER	Potter	5.9	1.5	15	1982	F	GBR
p	DH183	JOINT VENTURE	Potter	8.0	3.5	56	1982	F	GBR
p	DH384	DVFG	Angler	5.7	0.9	30	1992	F	GBR
p	DH387	TRUE GRIT	Potter	9.2	46.0	148	1999	F	GBR
p	DH390	NIL DESPERANDUM	Potter	9.0	5.1	49	1981	F	GBR
p	DH392	ELM	Angler	3.7	0.6	59	1999	F	GBR
p	DH405	DEEJAY	Netter				2005	F	GBR
p	LA604	SKIPPER'S WIFE	Out of Area	4.8	1.3	39	2001	F	GBR
p	LT70	EMILY ROSE	Trawler	9.9	6.7	82.0	1989	F	GBR
p	Ex PH473	SWIFT	De-registered	5.4	1.1	30.0	1989	F	GBR
p	PW449	GEORGE-D	Netter	7.0	1.6	160	1994	F	UNK
p	Ex PZ111	VERACITY (Replica)	Lugger Ketch	9.8					
p	SC66	HUSTLER	Potter	9.8	6.3	89	1975	F	GBR
	SE371	WEST WIND		4.4	0.7	11	1996	F	GBR

HMS Somerset & Britannia Naval College

BL31 Mischief - 31/07/2004

DH1 Nicky V - 26/03/2004

DH5 Wiiliam Henry II - 31/07/2004

DH8 Mayfly - 16/09/2005

DH17 Excel - 10/09/2005

DH20 Magnum - 15/05/2006

DH60 Maggie-Marie - 04/07/2005

DH63 Skerry Belle - 04/07/2005

DH76 Heatseeker - 16/09/2005

DH88 Rejoice - 16/09/2005

DH89 Bobolink - 16/09/2005

DH97 Full Monty - 29/042005

DH99 Superb-Us - 16/06/2006 (DL)

DH119 Northern Clipper - 16/09/2006

DH133 Damsel Fly - 16/092005

DH135 Our Pammy - 16/092005

DH141 Britannia of Beesands - 16/09/2005

DH149 Newbrook - 10/09/2005

DH179 Sea Soldier - 31/07/2004

DH183 Joint Venture - 15/05/2006

DH384 DVFG - 26/03/2004

DH387 True Grit - 22/09/2004

DH390 Nil Desperandum - 16/09/2005

DH392 Elm - 10/09/2005

DH405 Deejay - 15/05/2006

LA604 Skipper's Wife - 29/04/2005

LT70 Emily Rose - 25/062004

Ex PH473 Swift - 04/07/2005

PW449 George-D - 29/04/2005

Ex PZ111 Veracity - 19/04/2006

SC66 Hustler - 16/09/2005

TORCROSS

Slapton Sands at Torcross

The Sea Wall

The old records of Beesands show that there was a fish cellar at Torcross in 1584. Torcross is at the southern end of Slapton Sands, and the strip of land bearing the road north between the sandy shore and the lagoon behind it, has frequently been breached in easterly storms. The substantial sea defence walls behind the shingle beaches at Torcross were built between 1980 and 1990 to try and prevent easterly storm damage to the village. The lagoon is an Area of Special Scientific Interest as well as being an interesting reserve for bird life. It is fascinating to watch the small netters working from the beach, circling an area of sea, and then driving back right up onto the beach, after which the net is hauled ashore by hand from the beach in the manner of the old seiners. About six small potters and beach netters operate from the exposed shingle beach. The Local 'DH' Dartmouth registration predominates. Torcross houses the salvaged Sherman Tank, now a monument to the tragic loss by E boat action of about 700 American Marines preparing for D-Day in 1944, which was kept a close secret both during, and for many years after, the war.

Photo	Reg	VESSEL NAME	Type	LOA	Reg	ENG	Year	Hull	Nat
				Mtrs	Tons	Kw	Built		Built
p	DH21	ROB ROY	Netter	4.3	0.7	30	1982	F	GBR
p	DH77	DAWN	Netter	4.3	0.7	30	1978	F	GBR
p	DH86	DAWN RAIDER	Angler	4.5	0.8	30	1988	F	
p	DH92	P.W.S	Netter	4.4	0.8	30	1991	F	GBR
p	DH180	ZIGGY	Netter	3.9	0.9	30	1982	F	GBR
p	DH394	DIANNE T	Potter	4.0	0.7	16	1998	F	GBR

DH21 Rob Roy - 25/07/2004

DH77 Dawn - 10/09/2005

DH86 Dawn Raider - 10/09/2005

DH92 P.W.S. - 16/09/2005

DH180 Ziggy - 28/05/2005

DH394 Dianne T - 31/08/2003

61 BEESANDS

Beesands Shingle Beech

Beesands Slipway

Records of fishing from Beesands go back to 1588 and there have been fish cellars at both Beesands and Torcross. By the end of the 19th century up to 8 tons of crabs were being sent to London per week. A strong easterly storm completely destroyed the nearby fishing village of Hallsands in 1917 just a few miles further south of Beesands. This following continued dredging of shingle, both from the beach and offshore, which started in 1897. The shingle was used in Devonport construction work in Plymouth. Beesands is totally unprotected to the East, and like Torcross the seawalls were built between 1980 and 1990 to prevent easterly storm damage. In the winter the boats are hauled behind the sea walls for protection. About four small potters and beach netters operate from the Beesands shingle beach, which is the main fish landing place for both Torcross and Beesands boats.

BEESANDS FISHING VESSELS

Photo	Reg	VESSEL NAME	Type	LOA	Reg	ENG	Year	Hull	Nat
				Mtrs	Tons	Kw	Built		Built
p	DH11	MIRANDA	Netter	4.8	0.9	7	1982	F	UNK
p	DH15	ZOOM	Netter/ Potter	5.7	1.1	86	1983	F	GBR
p	DH62	MOONFLEET	Potter	5.6	1.1	59	1986	F	GBR
p	DH74	PISCES	Netter	4.9	1.2	22	1968	F	GBR
p	DH397	EBONY ROSE	Netter	4.27	0.73	15	1990	F	GBR
p	DH399	AHAB	Netter	4.7				F	GBR

DH11 Miranda - 28/05/2005

DH15 Zoom - 28/05/2005

DH62 Moonfleet - 25/07/2004

DH74 Pisces - 28/05/2005

DH397 Ebony Rose - 20/08/2003

DH399 Ahab - 10/09/2005

SALCOMBE

Salcombe Estuary from Snapes Point
Salcombe town on the right

The Fish Quay up Batson Creek

Since no river flows into it, the Salcombe (or Kingsbridge) estuary is not an estuary at all, but a 'Ria' or drowned valley, open to the sea. The entrance is well protected in most weather conditions, but there is a shallow shifting bar of sand just within the entrance. A combination of both southerly wind and swell on an ebb tide can cause dangerous conditions on this bar. Inside it there is ample water at all stages of the tide until halfway up the estuary towards Kingsbridge. Above the halfway point it dries out at low water. In the 19th century Salcombe had a thriving shipbuilding industry which declined as the demand for wooden vessels reduced. There was also significant trade to the Caribbean using local boats and crews. A fleet of some 40 fishing vessels, mainly crabbers and potters, now operates from Salcombe, and fishing also goes on within the entrance. About a dozen of them are around the ten metre length or more, and about 30 of them bear the Salcombe (SE) registration. The main fish quay is just to the north of Salcombe town, up Batson Creek, while many of the larger boats moor off Snapes Point which is a little further north. Snapes Point is National Trust land and affords a splendid view of Salcombe town, the estuary and the harbour. A few boats can sometimes be seen at the head of the 'estuary' at Kingsbridge. Salcombe is another port from which troops departed for D-Day.

Unusually empty view of Salcombe in the Winter

Sun rising over Snapes Point

SALCOMBE FISHING VESSELS

Photo	REG	VESSEL NAME	Type	LOA	Reg	Eng	Year	Hull	Nat
				-	Tons	Kw	Built	-	Built
p	BM476	LADY MAGGIE	Netter/Potter	5.9	2.4	17	1986	F	GBR
p	DH82	LUCKY DIP	Angler	4.5	0.1	7	1982	F	GBR
p	DH95	TENACIOUS	Trawler/Potter	15.1	21.5	131	1975	W	GBR
p	Ex PH487	VERITY	De-registered	5.0					
p	PW60	LITTLE PEARL	Netter/Potter	4.9	1.3	5	1980	F	GBR
p	PZ48	LORRAINE RUTH	Netter	4.8	0.9	16.0	1992	F	GBR
p	SE3	TWO BOYS	Angler	4.0					
p	SE5	ANGLO DAWN II	Angler	9.9	9.7	190	1983	F	GBR
p	SE11	SWIFT	Netter	4.83	0.64	14	1984	F	GBR
p	SE14	ANN	Liner	7.0	4.1	6	1924	W	GBR
p	SE15	KEVI-TOR-RU	Netter/Potter	6.1	1.7	20	1980	F	GBR
p	SE18	CHARLOTTE ANN	Netter/Potter	5.95	1.58	14	1998	F	GBR
p	Ex SE21	Tender Sou'West Lady	De-registered	5.0				W	
p	SE25	DUNLIN	Netter/Liner	6.2	2.7	12	1981	F	GBR
p	Ex SE26	TARKA	De-registered	<5					
p	SE33	PHOENIX	Potter	9.9	5.2	179	1979	F	GBR
p	SE34	PEN GLAS	Potter	16.5	62.0	216	1960	W	FRA
p	SE35	CRUSTACEAN	Netter	8.2	4.6	59	1971	W	GBR
p	SE46	OUTSETTER	Netter/Liner	6.5	4.0	25	1984	F	GBR
p	SE58	GEORGE EDWIN	Netter/Potter	10.5	11.5	100	1987	W	GBR
	SE71	TARDY	Netter	5.6	1.8	7	1973	F	GBR
p	SE74	SALCOMBE LASS	Netter/Potter	11.0	5.8	66	1966	W	GBR
	SE89	NEW HORIZON		5.8	1.1	29	1980	F	GBR
p	SE101	EMMA JANE	Potter	18.4	122.0	317	1989	S	NLD
p	SE122	GUILLEMOT	Netter/Potter	6.4	1.7	34	1995	F	GBR
p	SE138	MAY QUEEN	Liner	4.0	0.5	1		W	GBR
	SE142	NICKS		3.9	0.6	6	1986	F	GBR
p	SE150	CLAIRE LOUISE	Trawler/Potter	11.9	14.5	6	1978	W	GBR
p	SE154	BUNG	Potter	5.0	1.0	7	1965	W	GBR
p	SE156	ARTFUL DODGER III	Potter	6.3	3.2	192	1989	F	GBR
p	SE158	MARTLET	Angler	6.0	2.7	8	1946	W	GBR
p	SE328	LEO 2	Liner/Crabber	4.9	0.9	7	1973	G	GBR
p	SE330	EMILY ANN	Liner	4.5	0.7	4	1985	F	GBR
p	SE332	PEADAR ELAINE	Potter	18.3	127.0	261	1990	S	
p	SE333	MINSTRAL	Potter	5.5	1.7	7	1982	F	GBR
p	SE334	ELIZABETH	Angler	8.25	2.66	54	1978	F	
	SE343	TOUTAI		5.00	0.7	15	1990	F	GBR
p	WH461	DAVRIK I	Netter/Potter	9.8	6.7	89	1981	F	GBR
p	Ex WY788	CHRISTY G	De-registered	9.9	5.8	71	1987	S	GBR

BM476 Lady Maggie - 31/08/2005

DH82 Lucky Dip - 16/05/2006

DH95 Tenacious - 24/02/2005

Ex PH487 Verity - 12/05/2004

PW60 Little Pearl - 05/08/2004

PZ48 Lorraine Ruth - 02/10/2005

SE3 Two Boys - 07/11/2003

SE5 Anglo Dawn II - 16/05/2006

SE11 Swift - 22/102005

SE14 Ann - 21/11/2005

SE15 Kevi-Tor-Ru - 02/10/2005

SE18 Charlotte Ann - 22/10/2005

Ex SE21 TT Sou'West Lady - 31/08/2005

SE25 Dunlin - 03/01/2005

Ex SE26 Tarka - 04/02/2005

SE33 Phoenix - 15/03/2005

SALCOMBE

SE34 Pen Glas - 16/02/2006

SE35 Crustacean - 16/05/2006

SE46 Outsetter - 15/03/2005

SE58 George Edwin - 15/03/2005

SE74 Salcombe Lass - 02/10/2005

SE101 Emma Jane - 16/05/2006

SE122 Guillemot - 04/02/2005

SE138 May Queen - 04/02/2005

SE150 Claire Louise - 24/02/2005

SE154 Bung - 19/10/2004

SE156 Artful Dodger III - 16/05/2006

SE158 Martlet - 08/02/2004

SE328 Leo 2 - 24/02/2005

SE330 Emily Ann - 02/10/2005

SE332 Peadar Elaine - 16/05/2006

SE333 Minstral - 08/02/2004

SE334 Elizabeth - 02/10/2005

WH461 Davrik I - 16/06/2006

Ex WY788 Christy G - 15/03/2005

63 HOPE COVE & BIGBURY

Inner Hope with old Lifeboat House

The Breakwater - Bolt Head Beyond

The village of Hope first got a historical mention in 1281, and the Cove was originally known as Pilchard Cove   It is located just North East of Bolt Head and consists of two bays divided by the prominent 'Shippen Rock' on which one of the Spanish Armada fleet went ashore in 1588.   That was only one of several vessels which came to grief on this treacherous coastline. In the 1750s it was reported that one boat brought ashore in excess of 20,000 mackerel in one 'draught' alone.   The northern bay called Outer Hope is just an attractive beach, and the southern Bay - Inner Hope - is a more sheltered beach with a protective low breakwater over which the high tide laps .   Both are very exposed to

Hope Cove Inner

The Old Fish Quay - Hope Cove

the prevailing South Westerlies. Seine fishing was carried out from here in the 19th century, but it was also well known for brandy smuggling from France. The occasional potter from Salcombe can be seen in the Cove but there are now no longer any registered boats operating. An active seine fishery also operated from Challaborough, some five miles north west of Hope Cove and just west of Bigbury on Sea. Reports on the herring shoals came from the prominent lookout on Burgh Island. All signs at Challaborough have vanished, but the 14th century Pilchard Inn on Burgh Island is a reminder of days past. Though it was never a port, continental trade went on from the beaches here as early as 300AD, tin from Dartmoor being exported. A small potter fishing vessel is kept on a farm at Bigbury on Sea, and trailer launched from the beach near Burgh Island.

The Pilchard Inn

HOPE COVE & BIGBURY FISHING VESSELS

Photo	REG	VESSEL NAME	Type	LOA	Reg	Eng	Year	Hull	Nat
					Tons	Kw	Built		Built
p	Ex SE8	EMMA JO	De-registered	5.6				F	GBR
p	Ex SE9	GIRL JEAN II	De-registered	8.13	5.31	45	1978	W	GBR
p	TH287	LEONORA	Potter	6.0	2.1	56	1995	F	GBR

Ex SE8 Emma Jo - 31/082005

Ex SE9 Girl Jean II - 07/11/2003

BIGBURY on SEA

TH287 Leonora - 12/02/2006

64 RIVER YEALM

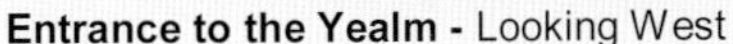

Entrance to the Yealm - Looking West

'The Pool' at the End of Newton Creek

The twin towns of Noss Mayo (originally Noss Major) and Newton Ferrers (originally Ferris) date back to the 14th century. They are on the drying out mile long Newton Creek which branches off from the River Yealm itself. Fishing is recorded as being the major occupation for the residents of the twin towns facing each other on the creek and there is still good fishing, and oyster beds in the River. It is a very attractive unspoilt river befitting the Celtic origins of its name 'Yealme' meaning 'kind'. Five fishing vessels can be found either in 'The Pool' at the entrance to Newton Creek opposite Warren Point or further up in the moorings above the marked oyster beds. There is a sand bar across the entrance and a narrow marked channel close in to the southern shore to get round it. The combination of the bar and the prominent 'Mewstone Rock' to the West give good protection once inside the harbour from major seas but it can be very gusty and a very tricky harbour to enter or leave under sail alone.

RIVER YEALM FISHING VESSELS

Photo	Reg	Vessel Name	Type	LOA Meters	Reg Tons	Eng Kw	Year	Hull	Nat Build
p	BM392	MAGGIE	Potter	5.60	1.3	41	1997	F	GBR
p	IH68	LAURA ANNE	Potter	7.30	2.4	63	1988	F	GBR
p	PH589	MAVERICK	Liner/Angler	9.45	3.5	90	1995	F	GBR
p	PH5568	CHALLENGE	Netter	8.13	4.5	58	1986	F	GBR
p	SC80	VIOLET MAY	Netter/Potter	5.80	1.3	16	1997	F	GBR

BM492 Maggie - 17/05/2006

IH68 Laura Ann - 08/10/2004

PH589 Maverick - 17/05/2006

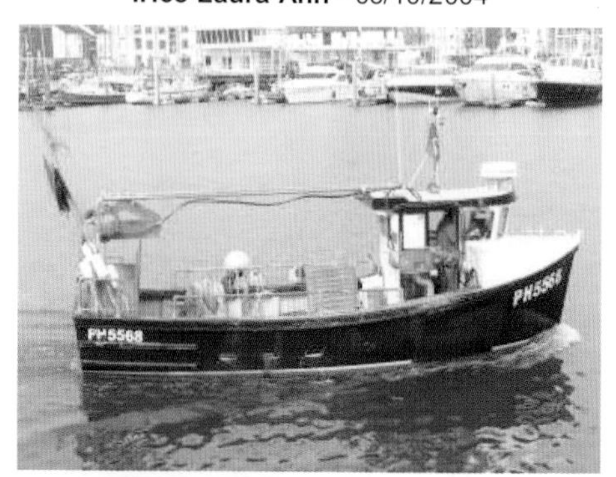

PH5568 Challenge - 29/03/2006

SC80 Violet May - 17/05/2006

Bluebells at the Mouth of the River Yealm

65 PLYMOUTH

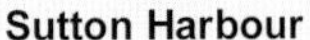
Sutton Harbour

Plymouth Breakwater from Cornwall

Although Plymouth dates back to 1231, the modern City of Plymouth is surprisingly recent, having been formed by the combination of Devonport, Plymouth, and Stonehouse in 1914. The area later to become Plymouth is described in a manuscript of the time of Henry II as "A mene thing, an inhabitation for fishars." Plympton was the original old town in the area and also the major port for the mining industry on Dartmoor, but as the River Plym silted up, the village of Sutton, which prior to the late 12th century had been a small fishing and agricultural village at the mouth of the River Plym, became the major commercial and fishing port. Sutton harbour's use by military and commercial shipping increased with the acquisition of the provinces in South West France by Henry II, but because of its exposure to the prevailing Sou'Westerly winds it was a virtual trap for sailing vessels, and for the Navy it was always overshadowed by the more sheltered anchorages of Dartmouth and Torbay.

It was from Plymouth that Francis Drake set out in 1577 to circumnavigate the globe returning to a knighthood in 1580. It was also the point of departure for several pioneers such as James Cook, Charles Darwin, and the Pilgrim Fathers on their way to America in 1620, (though they did make a further stop in Newlyn apparently because the water they had picked up in Plymouth was foul). The choice of Plymouth, rather than Dartmouth as the naval base, was probably because Sir Francis Drake's home was near Plymouth, and the influence of the Plymouth born Sir John Hawkins, who was Treasurer of the Navy from 1578-89, and Comptroller from 1589-95. Plymouth Hoe was also the site of Sir Francis Drake's well known 'Bowling Story' when the Spanish Armada was spotted approaching, from what is known as the 'chapel' on Rame Head to the west of Plymouth. The 'chapel' possibly acted as a lookout point for the herring shoals at the start of the herring season and on sighting them the drifter fleet at Cawsand would be alerted. Such a warning would have been superfluous at a time during the Civil War, when Plymouth under the Parliamentarians was besieged by Royalist forces, and the hunger of the inhabitants was relieved by what is called the 'Miracle of the Barbican'. Thousands of pilchards swam right into Sutton Harbour where they could easily be swept up in any sort of receptacle, even buckets and kettles! Turnchapel is on the south bank of the "Cattewater" (see Map over), and was described in the late 18th century as being 'Sheltered from the weather by the Mount Batten peninsular to the West and the hill on which the Citadel stands opposite it at the entrance to the Cattewater. The ancient fortress of the Citadel would have provided a military defence for this area which thus would have provided a good anchorage,

Close up of Sutton Fish Harbour

Map of Plymouth Sound showing location of Plymouth

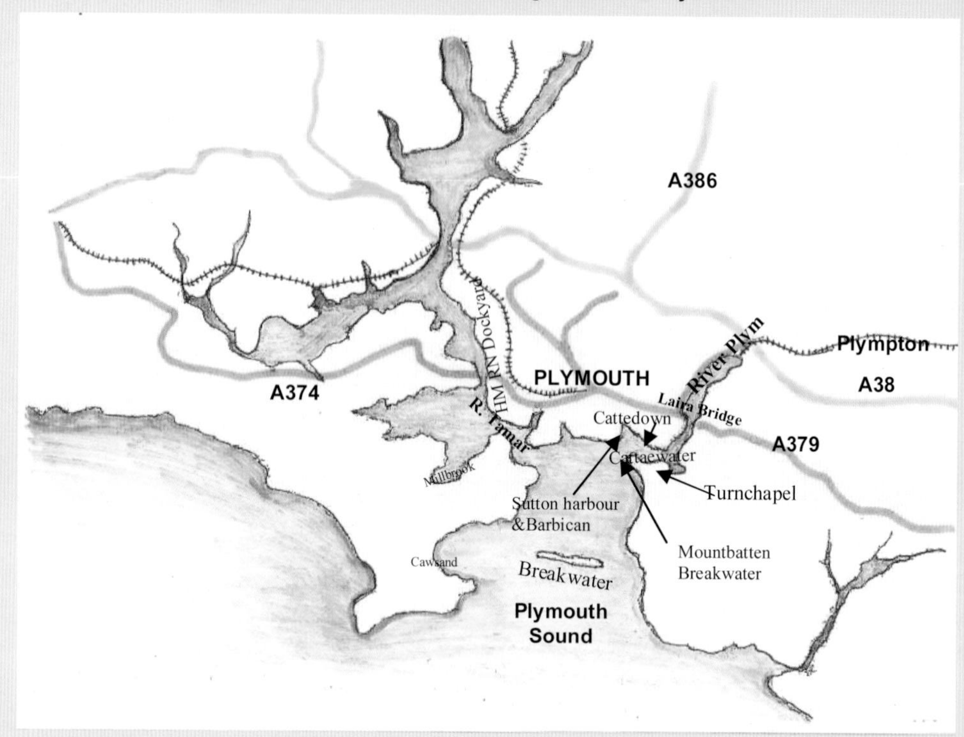

was sheltered from the worst of the weather and given military protection from any enemy.' (Mainly the Spanish followed by the French) . This was in the days of sail, and well before the Mount Batten or even the Plymouth breakwaters were constructed.

In the early 19th century the historic village of Cawsand, on the Cornwall side of Plymouth Sound, supported a fleet of some 40 drifters, and seven seine fisheries, at a time when Plymouth had only six craft and Turnchapel nine. However in 1843 The 'Housekeepers Guide to the Fish Market' Plymouth, described the 62 Plymouth area boats as being mainly sloop rigged trawlers of up to 50 tons, but some smaller and yawl rigged, all with crews of three men and a boy. The comment was made on the poor qualities of catch and the numbers of young fish landed, and that it was to be 'Deeply regretted that this species of fishing should be conducted by men of such reckless proceedings'.!!! There were obviously no fishery Patrol Boats monitoring the fishing industry then.

Like the River Plym the River Tamar was also a major water access for mining and agriculture, but apart from an early pilchard seine at Saltash and some oyster beds was not generally used for fishing. Devonport was established as a naval base in 1691 but was only developed as a major naval dockyard during the wars against the French in the late 18th and early 19th centuries, and was never a fishing port. As part of the naval build up at this time, the mile long breakwater was constructed using French POW labour between 1812 -1851 under the guidance of the well known engineer John Rennie, making navigation into

Fisheries Patrol Boat - 'Drumbeat Of Devon'

The Beacon on the Breakwater

Plymouth straightforward in any weather conditions. The beacon on the eastern end of the breakwater has a six foot diameter circular cage at the top in which it is said that up to six mariners shipwrecked on the breakwater could climb up into, in order to take refuge from the seas. There is no record of it ever having been used however. Additional protection to Sutton harbour was provided by the Mount Batten Breakwater which was built in 1881.

In 1906 a company set up a small factory on the Mount Batten Peninsular called the 'Plymouth Fish Guano and Oil Company' using fish waste provided from Sutton Harbour opposite. The smell was so appalling that an injunction was served in 1912 to close it down but it only finally closed down in 1917.

A description in 1957 noted that "The Cattewater is a trawling ground off the RAF Mount Batten *(Then still a flying boat base but now closed)* with a smooth rocky bottom, useful for prawns during the summer. A ground more frequently trawled was the main channel between Oreston *(near Turnchapel)* and Laira Bridge, " *(where the A379 crosses the river Plym - see map)*. He also noted that there was a regular supply of the green crab, as well as shrimps). It mentions shoals of mysids *(Cuttle fish)* occurring there, as well as farther up the estuary, and states that they may be taken with a hand-net."

The protecting piers to Sutton Pool were completed in 1799, but caused the harbour to silt up, and it was a drying out harbour until the piers were extended, and the lock constructed in 1993. Approximately 5,000 square metres of land has been reclaimed in Sutton Harbour since 1992 and the harbour is no longer tidal. The original fish quay was on the Barbican side, and what is now the glassware retail outlet used to be the fish market. Following the construction of the lock and the new fish market on the east side of Sutton Harbour in 1995, Plymouth has become one of the major landing places for fishing vessels from all over the United Kingdom. It is a significant landing place for scallops.

Almost 100 fishing vessels are actually based in Plymouth waters from the smallest potters to the two largest vessels, Wiron 1 & 2, which at 51m length and 1068 tons, are too large to enter Sutton Harbour and use the commercial dock at Victoria Pier in Cattedown. About 65 of them bear the Plymouth (PH) registration. The majority of the local fishing vessels can be found in Sutton Harbour though isolated vessels are scattered around the Plymouth waters. Three or four are sometimes moored just below the Laira Bridge on the River Plym or near the slipway at Turnchapel. Several craft are also based close to Millbrook in a creek on the west side of the River Tamar. The Tamar based fishing boats are covered in the sister book to this 'The Fishing Boats and Ports of Cornwall'. Some oyster trawling is still occasionally carried out on the RiverTamar by a few vessels from Sutton harbour.

Apart from pioneers like Drake and Hawkins, other less well known adventurers have crossed the seas from Plymouth as evidenced by the fact that there are now some 400 places over the world with the name of Plymouth, all inspired by the original Plymouth in Devon.

The Breakwater & Lighthouse

"Upon the British coast what ship yet ever came that, not of Plymouth hears, where the brave navies lie?"
from Polyolbion by Michael Drayton (15th Century Poet)

PLYMOUTH FISHING VESSELS

Photo	Reg	VESSEL NAME	Type	LOA Mtrs	Reg Tons	Eng Kw	Year Built	Hull	Nat Build
p	AH101	GIRL SOO	Potter	6.60	2.41	8	-	G	GBR
p	BM100	Cheryl of Ladram (Ex Centaur)	Beam Trawler	30.3	232.0	858	1980	S	NLD
p	BM361	BARENTSZEE	Beam Trawler	30.55	220.0	709	1984	S	BEL
p	CF1	NEMESIS	Scalloper	9.94	23.7	112	1996	S	GBR
p	CL22	DON VALLEY	Trawler/Scalloper	9.80	14.7	134	1992	S	GBR
p	E14	HEART OF OAK	Potter	9.99	4.7	58	1968	W	GBR
p	E88	Margaret of Ladram (Ex J588)	Beam Trawler	32.00	92.0	610	1974	S	NLD
p	E161	OUR ENDEAVOUR	Trawler	9.95	13.1	128	1988	F	GBR
p	E225	JOY of LADRAM(ExJ225)	Beam Trawler	37.75	373.0	1492	1987	S	NLD
p	FH625	BOY JACK II	Liner	4.52	9.47	93	1989	F	GBR
p	FH636	CORNISH GEM	Scalloper	9.50	17.0	106	1996	S	GBR
p	FY3	STORM CHILD	Liner	7.17	4.6	50	1989	W	GBR
p	FY95	CRISTAL WATERS	Trawler/Scalloper	9.99	9.63	89	1969	W	FRA
p	FY276	ZADOK	Trawler/Netter	9.90	9.2	187	1976	F	GBR
p	H105	EXCELSIOR	Netter	9.96	7.6	239	1990	F	GBR
p	HL125	BOY SCOTT (Ex Chatterbox)	Netter	6.4	2.8	22	1992	F	GBR
p	HL1061	GIRL EMMA	Netter/Potter	6.43	3.1	22	1991	F	GBR
p	J192	PIETERJE	De-registered	26.20	92.8	611	1971	S	NLD
p	J217	FRANCES OF LADRAM (ExPZ100)	De-registered	25.20	83.0	221	1957	S	NED
p	ExJ219	EVERT MARUTJE	Motor Yacht	26.40	107.7	368	1968	S	NLD
p	Ex J535	PIETER	De-registered	26.00	116.0	589	1969	S	NLD
p	LL271	DOLPHIN	Scalloper	9.80	5.7	89	1991	S	GBR
p	Ex M313	FOXY LADY	De-registered	8.5	2.5	167	1981	F	GBR
p	M560	DIGNITY	Netter	7.90	8.0	45	1985	F	GBR
p	MBA	MBA SEPIA	Research Trawler	15.24				F	GBR
p	MEEU8	PLYMOUTH QUEST	Research Trawler				2001	S	CHI
p	Ex NN88	SELINA ANN	De-registered	10.93	13.5	130	1989	S	GBR
p	PE477	ANTON	Netter	6.14	1.90	55	1987	F	GBR
p	Ex PE524	ENDEAVOUR	De-registered	8.00	7.0	90	1975	W	GBR
p	PH2	SECRET STAR	Angler	8.00			2005	F	GBR
p	PH12	CARLA MAY	Potter	7.20	5.1	37	1972	U	GBR
p	PH34	TAMESIS II	Angler	9.95	4.2	224		G	
p	Ex PH48	LANCER	De-registered	7.15	3.0	42	1981	F	GBR
p	PH60	WARRIOR	Angler	9.50	6.3	167	1989	F	GBR
p	PH79	SWEET HOME	De-registered	8.46	5.63	59	1952	W	GBR
p	ExPH90	SQUILLA	De-registered	19.7	73	238	1973	S	GBR
p	PH98	KITTIWAKE	De-registered	9.00					
p	PH99	FRANJO A	Trawler	11.40	13.3	110	1979	W	GBR

PLYMOUTH

p	PH110	WIRON 1	Pelagic Trawler	51.44	1059.0	2160	1995	S	ESP
p	PH117	TRIO	Angler	9.60	7.0	89	1982	F	GBR
p	PH122	BOSLOE	Netter/Potter	14.39	18.4	94	1966	W	GBR
p	PH160	COMPASS ROSE	Potter	8.24	4.5	31	1956	W	UNK
p	Ex PH167	ANDERTON LADY	De-registered	7.13	4.6	43	1983	F	GBR
p	Ex PH207	GAMMARUS	De-registered					W	
p	PH220	WIRON 2	Pelagic Trawler	51.44	1068.0	2160	1996	S	ESP
p	ExPH221	JONTINE	De-registered	6.10	2.8	7	1900	W	GBR
p	Ex PH224	WESTERN ENTERPRISE	De-registered						
p	PH245	PAULINE J	Out of Area	9.98	10.4	95	1987	F	GBR
p	PH254	BRENDA C	Potter	9.30	4.4	89	1973	F	GBR
p	PH271	KELLY J	Angler	7.32	3.3	39	1978	F	GBR
p	PH277	CHILTERN BOY	Potter	7.52	2.2	59	1964	F	GBR
p	Ex PH299	FLYING FRECKLES	De-registered	7.17	2.2	26	1979	F	GBR
p	PH307	SPLENDOUR	Netter	7.50	2.9	56	1988	F	GBR
p	PH316	DARTER	Netter	9.75	7.0	73	1974	F	GBR
p	PH322	METAN	Potter/Liner	8.29	5.3	111	1980	F	GBR
p	PH330	ADMIRAL GORDON	Beam Trawler	22.21	137.0	220	1988	S	NLD
p	PH344	JESSIE LOU	Scalloper/Netter	12.49	12.0	231	1987	F	GBR
p	PH350	SAMPHIRE	Angler	7.20	5.2	48	1980	F	GBR
p	PH411	SILVER STREAM	Trawler	14.55	27.4	119	1966	W	FRA
p	PH429	SHELLEY MARIE	Trawler/Scalloper	11.62	27.3	179	1988	S	GBR
p	Ex PH431	GAVIOTA N	De-registered	6.25	2.7	31	1962	W	GBR
p	PH440	ADMIRAL BLAKE	Beam Trawler	22.20	136.0	220	1989	S	NLD
p	Ex PH452	SHERLMAR	Sank Aug 2005	10.30	11.5	134	1980	F	GBR
p	Ex PH463	TIBURON	De-registered						
p	Ex PH491	AMOCO	De-registered	9.95	8.1	138	1979	F	GBR
p	PH530	KATRINA	Liner	6.40	2.6	13	1986	F	GBR
p	PH550	ADMIRAL GRENVILLE	Beam Trawler	23.97	152.0	220	2001	S	NLD
p	PH564	ISABELLA	Netter/Potter	6.79	2.57	13	1976	W	GBR
p	PH574	KINSMAN	Stern Trawl	9.98	19.8	221	1992	S	GBR
p	Ex PH579	TIDDLER	De-registered	7.44	3.6	27	1992	F	GBR
p	PH584	OUR LOUISE	Out of Area	9.60	17.84	112	1995	F	GBR
p	PH585	SHIRALEE	Crabber	8.20	4.2	60	1963	W	FRA
p	PH586	GWALARN	Scalloper	9.95	14.3	116	1965	W	FRA
p	PH587	BELLE ETOILE	Trawl/Scalloper	9.30	5.4	90	1970	W	GBR
p	PH589	MAVERICK	Angler	9.45	3.5	90	1995	F	GBR
p	PH598	LISA LEANNE	Scalloper	9.60	9.8	90	1996	F	GBR
p	PH650	NORTHERN LASS	Potter	7.37	2.2	59	1986	F	
p	PH959	RICHARD ANN	Netter	9.99	9.9	112	1996	F	GBR
p	PH961	ExLADY JANE (LK780 Merlin)	Out of Area	9.99	10.7	135	1997	F	GBR
p	Ex PH962	D J	De-registered	9.95	7.0	72	1984	S	

PLYMOUTH

p	PH989	BARBICAN LADY	Trawler	9.92	9.0	95	1997	F	GBR
p	PH5557	EMMA LOUISE	Netter	9.90	10.5	82	1998	F	GBR
p	PH5561	KATHERINE M	Trawler/Scalloper	10.00	9.3	127	1999	S	GBR
p	PH5573	HARRIER	Potter	6.50	3.0	31	1980	W	GBR
p	ExPH5575	LARK	De-registered	6.10	0.9	6	1992	F	GBR
p	PH5577	MY DIANNE	Angler	5.80	1.51	30	1987	U	
p	PH5578	PETITE FOLIE	Scalloper	9.10	8.86	125	1974	W	FRA
p	PH5579	OCEAN BREEZE	De-registered	8.38	2.20	199	1980	U	GBR
p	PH5583	HANNAH JACK	Netter	9.8	7.8	74	2003	F	GBR
p	PH5587	BOUNTY	Angler	9.80	3.0	90	2005	F	GBR
p	PH5590	FAIR TRADE	Net/Potter	7.01	4.49	16	1979	F	GBR
p	PW32	CORNISH GEM	Potter	8.35	4.8	111	1984	F	GBR
p	PW186	SHEILA PAT	Potter	8.10	4.0	68	1977	F	GBR
p	Ex PW459	DIRE STRAITS	De-registered	7.60	3.3	63	1981	F	GBR
p	PZ15	SPAVEN MOR (Ex Porthleven)	Potter	6.58	1.7	4	2003	F	GBR
p	PZ1015	RACHEL & VICTORIA	Netter	5.55	1.7	6	1995	F	GBR
p	Ex RX39	LISA ANN	De-registered	12.80	32.0	186	1989	S	GBR
p	Ex RX155	HERCULES	De-registered	13.9	28.9	221	1988	S	GBR
p	SE2	SEA VIXEN	Netter/Potter	6.90	2.7	12	1968	W	GBR
p	SS142	CARRIE-ANN LADY	Crabber	6.15	1.2	22	1982	F	GBR
p	SS272	ALISON	De-registered	4.80	1.1	10	1969	F	GBR
p	Ex TH12	GYPSY MERMAID	Gaff Ketch	12.20			1965	W	GBR
p	TH24	MIDNIGHT SUN	Trawler	11.99	27.3	160	1996	F	GBR
p	WH707	ZARANATHAX	Trawler	9.80	12.9	14.3	1979	W	
p	WK799	CARLY ANNE	Netter	7.70	4.6	57	1991	F	GBR

A Helping hand Homewards!

AH101 Girl Soo - 29/03/2006

BM100 Cheryl of Ladram - 20/062006

BM361 Barentzee - 12/02/2006

CF1 Nemesis - 09/08/2006

CL22 Don Valley - 05/07/2004

E14 Heart of Oak - 20/07/2005

E88 Margaret of Ladram - 25/06/2006

E161 Our Endeavour - 11/06/2005

FH625 Boy Jack - 07/09/2005

FH636 Cornish Gem - 07/12/2005

FY3 Storm Child - 17/05/2006

FY95 Cristal Waters - 03/04/2006

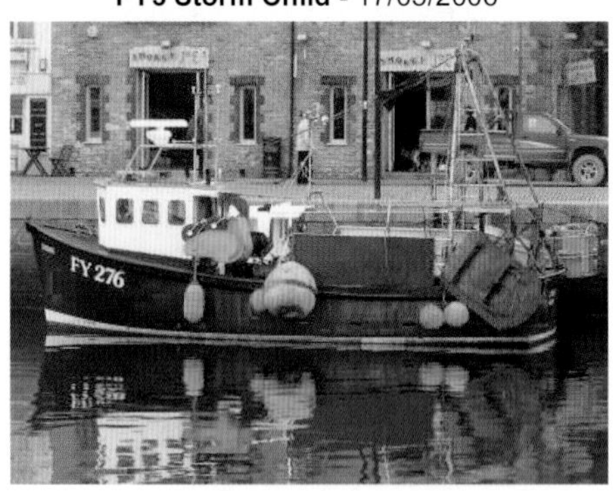

FY276 Zadok - 17/03/2004

H105 Excelsior - 07/05/2006

HL125 Boy Scott - 29/03/2006

HL1061 Girl Emma - 07/03/2005

Ex J192 Pieterje - 10/09/2004

J217 Frances of Ladram - 05/06/2004

Ex J219 Evert Marutje - 07/05/2004

Ex J535 Pieter - 04/09/2003

LL271 Dolphin - 11/06/2005

Ex M313 Foxy Lady - 04/07/2004

M560 Dignity - 25/07/2006

MBA Sepia - 17/11/2004

MEEU8 Plymouth Quest - 08/11/2004

Ex NN88 Selina Ann - 03/09/2003

PE477 Anton - 08/02/2006

Ex PE524 Endeavour- 25/08/2004

PH2 Secret Star - 11/06/2005

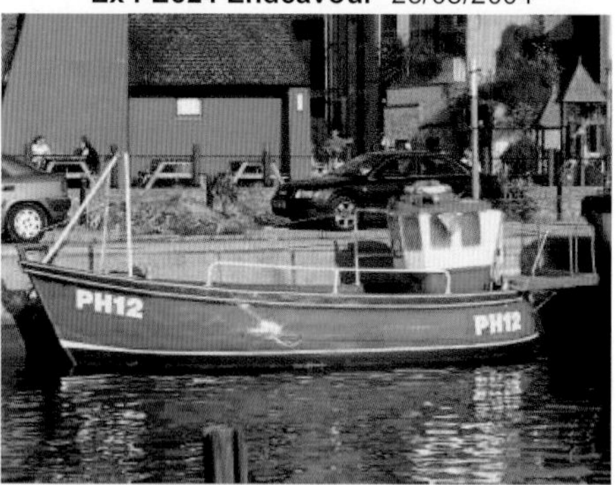

PH12 Carla May - 20/05/2004

PH34 Tamesis II - 20/07/2005

PH48 Lancer - 24/11/2003

PH60 Warrior - 03/06/2006

Ex PH79 Sweet Home– 29/08/2003

Ex PH90 Squilla - 16/11/2003

Ex PH98 Kittiwake - 31/10/2003

PH99 Franjo A - 11/06/2005

PH110 Wiron I - 08/10/2004

PH117 Trio - 03/06/2006

PH122 Bosloe - 24/03/2005

PH160 Compass Rose - 15/07/2005

Ex PH167 Anderton Lady - 29/11/2003

Ex PH207 Gammarus - 22/05/2005

PH220 Wiron 2 - 07/09/2004

Ex PH221 Jontine - 23/11/2004

Ex PH224 Western Enterprise - 11/10/2004

PH245 Pauline J - 14/11/2003

PH254 Brenda C - 18/09/2005

PH271 Kelly J - 07/05/2006

PH277 Chiltern Boy - 11/05/2006

Ex PH299 Flying Freckles - 23/06/2004

PH307 Splendour - 03/04/2006

PH316 Darter - 07/02/2006

PH322 Metan - 08/07/2005

PH330 Admiral Gordon - 02/07/2004

PH344 Jessie Lou - 05/09/2004

PH350 Samphire - 20/07/2005

PH411 Silver Stream - 14/06/2005

PH429 Shelley Marie - 05/07/2004

Ex PH431 Gavio-Tan - 31/10/2003

PH440 Admiral Blake - 30/07/2005

Ex PH452 Sherlmar - 25/09/2004

Ex PH463 Tiburon - 24/06/2006

PH491 Amoco - 16/04/2005

PH530 Katrina - 29/03/2006

PH550 Admiral Grenville - 03/06/2006

PH564 Isabella - 27/06/2006

PH574 Kinsman - 19/07/2005

Ex PH579 Tiddler - 11/10/2004

PH584 Our Louise - 31/08/2004

PH586 Gwarlan - 20/05/2004

PH587 Belle Etoile - 07/05/2006

PH598 Lisa Leanne - 13/07/2006

PH650 Northern Lass - 07/12/2005

PH959 Richard Ann - 29/03/2006

Ex PH961 Lady Jane - 19/07/2005

PH962 D J - 20/06/2004

PH989 Barbican Lady - 28/05/2006

PH5557 Emma Louise - 07/03/2006

PH5561 Katherine M - 16/04/2005

PH5573 Harrier - 16/04/2005

Ex PH5575 Lark - 22/05/2005

PH5577 My Dianne - 30/08/2003

PH5578 Petite Folie - 03/04/2006

Ex PH5579 Ocean Breeze - 17/09/2004

PH5583 Hannah Jack - 03/04/2006

PH5587 Bounty - 30/072005

PH5590 Fair Trade - 05/07/2006

PW32 Cornish Gem - 23/11/2004

PW186 Sheila Pat - 13/06/2005

Ex PW459 Dire Straits - 29/07/2004

PZ15 Spaven Mor - 28/05/2006

PZ1015 Rachael & Victoria - 14/05/2006

Ex RX39 Lisa Ann - 03/02/2005

Ex RX155 Hercules - 12/10/2004

SE2 Sea Vixen - 27/08/2006

SS142 Carrie-Ann Lady - 20/01/2005

ExSS272 Alison - 30/09/2003

Ex TH12 Gipsy Mermaid - 11/06/2005

TH24 Midnight Sun - 07/05/2006

WH707 Zaranathx - 29/07/2004

WK799 Carly Ann - 15/07/2005

A Crowded Sutton Harbour

VISITING FISHING VESSELS to the SOUTH WEST

The following boats have been seen visiting various harbours in the South West Many of the Scallopers are seen annually during the summer months, but others may have been visiting on a one-off basis. The list is not exhaustive and only includes those boats that have been seen by the author.

SOUTH WEST VISITING FISHING VESSELS

Photo	Home Port	Reg	Name	Type	LOA	Reg	Eng	Year	Hull	Nat
					Mtrs	Tons	Kw	Built		Build
p	KIRKUDBRIGHT	BA87	KING CHALLENGER	Scalloper	21.3	192	536	2006	S	GBR
p	BUCKIE	BCK81	KESTREL	Scalloper	30.21	180.0	925	1973	S	NED
p	BUCKIE	BCK222	EMILY JANE	Scalloper	36.00	317.0	895	1988	S	NED
p	ABERDEEN	BS186	TJEERD JACKOBA	Scalloper	26.30	104.8	530	1968	S	NED
p	IRELAND	D592	IRISH ROSE	Trawler	29				S	
p	KIRKUDBRIGHT	DS10	ALBION	Scalloper	34.90	375.0	883	1985	S	NED
p	KIRKUDBRIGHT	DS11	VERTROUWEN	Scalloper	26.24	144.5	550	1968	S	NED
p	FRASERBURGH	FR59	GOLDEN GAIN V	Pair Trawler	25.70	222.0	530	1989	S	FRA
p	FRASERBURGH	FR317	OCEAN CREST	Trawler	14.95	40.0	298	2003	S	FRA
p	FRASERBURGH	FR347	OCEAN DAWN	Pair Trawler	26.50	224.0	619	1987	S	FRA
p	FRASERBURGH	FR359	SUNRISE	Pair Seiner	26.00	201.0	503	1984	S	GBR
p	FRASERBURGH	FR491	SERENE	Purse Seiner	17.9	38	809	1978	S	NOR
p	FRASERBURGH	FR821	SILVER STAR	Ring netter	18.00			1990	S	GBR
p	FRASERBURGH	FR894	OCEAN STAR	Trawler	14.95	40.0	298	2003	S	FRA
p	PETERHEAD	FR951	CARISANNE II	Trawler	23.00	176.0	310	1984	W	GBR
p	GUERNSEY	GU74	MARAUNDEUS	Trawler	15.2	26	179	1970	W	FRA
p	GUERNSEY	GU116	AMY BLUE	Netter	14.63				S	
p	GRIMSBY	GY341	IYSHA	Netter	18.80	39.6	186	1977	W	DEN
p	HOLYHEAD	H1074	NATALIE B	Scalloper	26.45	110.0	373	1967	S	NED
p	PETERHEAD	INS292	COURAGEOUS III	Pair Seiner	25.90	177.0	462	1980	S	DEN
p	STONEHAVEN	J86	FLEUR De FRANCE	Potter	19.13	18	214	1976	W	FRA
p	GRIMSBY	J235	KERLOCH	Potter	17.31	50.6	179	1959	W	FRA
p	NEWPORT	NT28	SEAPIE	Trawler	9.88	8.5	90	1991	F	GBR
p	PETERHEAD	PD220	AQUILA	Trawler	21.80	158.0	402	1988	W	GBR
p	PETERHEAD	PD313	ROSEMOUNT	Pair Seiner	26.00	176.0	447	1983	S	GBR
p	AYR	PD905	HONEYBOURNE III	Scalloper	29.16	215.0	588	1982	S	NED
p	PETERHEAD	PD959	DEMARES	Pair Seiner	24.50	171.0	369	1984	W	GBR
p	KILLYBEGS	SO958	ETERNAL DAWN	Pair Trawler	22.75	19.8	485	2005	S	IRE
p	STORNOWAY	SY16	JACAMAR II	Trawler	9.66	7.2	168		F	
p	KIRKUDBRIGHT	TN2	TOBRACH-N	Scalloper	23.07	147.0	500	1999	S	GBR
p	KIRKUDBRIGHT	TN36	MATTANJA	Beam Trawl	32.00	217.0	746	1973	S	NED
p	KIRKUDBRIGHT	TN37	PHILOMENA	Scalloper	30.57	165	662	1970	S	NED
p	KIRKUDBRIGHT	TN38	GEORGE LOU-N	Scalloper	25.5	142	142	1978	S	GBR
p	TROON	TN39	PIEDRAS	Trawler	35.50	295		1976	S	SPA
p	TOBERMORY	TT256	WESTERN BELLE	Scalloper	26.60	97.2	222	1961	S	NED
p	KILMORE QUAY	WD87	MOLLY B	Beam Trawler	35.50	356	1570	1989	S	GBR
p	WEXFORD	WD137	ENTERPRISE 1	Mussel Dredger	32.2	128	403	1981	S	NED
p	KILMORE QUAY	WD149	ALICIA	Beam Trawler	34.41	247	1007	1973	S	NED
p	ARKLOW	WD220	MARY KATE	Beam Trawler	24.45	92	223	1985	S	NED

BA87 King Challenger - 26/08/2006

BCK81 Kestrel - 30/06/2004

BCK222 Emily Jane - 23/05/2005

BS186 Tjeerd Jackoba - 22/06/2004

D592 Irish Rose - 24/01/2005

DS10 Albion - /31/05/2006

DS11 Vertrouwen - 08/04/2005

FR59 Golden Gain V - 30/03/2004

FR317 Ocean Crest - 15/11/2004

FR347 Ocean Dawn - 12/04/2004

FR359 Sunrise - 05/04/2004

FR821 Silver Star - 20/12/2005

FR894 Ocean Star - 17/11/2004

FR951 Carisanne II - 29/03/2004

GU74 (Ex BM192) **Maraundeus -** 04/07/2005

GU116 Amy Blue - 01/02/2006

GY341 Iyisha - 11/03/2004

H1074 Natalie B - 07/07/2006

INS292 Courageous III - 12/04/2004

J86 Fleur de France - 01/04/2006

J235 Kerloch - 21/02/2006

NT28 Seapie - 16/04/2005

PD220 Aquilla - 30/03/2004

PD313 Rosemount - 19/03/2004

PD905 Honeybourne III - 31/05/2006

PD959 Demares - 30/03/2004

SO958 Eternal Dawn - 07/03/2006

SY16 Jacamar II - 03/10/2005

TN2 Tobrach-N - 30/07/2006

TN36 Mattanja - 29/04/2004

TN37 Philomena - 25/03/2005

TN38 George Lou-N - 07/09/2004

South West VISITORS

Ex TN39 Piedras - 05/10/2005

WD87 Molly B - 24/09/2005

WD137 Enterprise I - 11/08/2006

WD149 Alicia - 02/03/2005

WD220 Mary Kate - 26/04/2005

Sorting catch on board

		DEVON & CORNWALL ALPHABETICAL	
p	E19	(Unnamed)	Exmouth
p	Ex PZ1	3 Girls	Sennen Cove
p	PZ203	A B S	Newlyn
p	PZ198	Aaltje Adriaantje	Newlyn
p	P483	Ability	Mevagissey
p	Ex PZ679	Acilla	Mousehole
p	E282	Adbrenat	Beer
p	BM79	Adela	Brixham
p	SH279	Adella (Ex Jodan C)	Newlyn
p	PH440	Admiral Blake	Plymouth
p	PH330	Admiral Gordon	Plymouth
p	PH550	Admiral Grenville	Plymouth
p	DH399	Ahab	Torcross
p	AH32	Ajax	Newlyn
p	Ex PH5546	Albatross	Ex Brixham
p	DS10	Albion	Visitor
p	NN138	Aleyna	Brixham
p	PZ199	Algrie	Newlyn
p	E516	Alibi	Appledore/Exmouth
p	TH37	Alice	Teignmouth
p	PZ592	Alice Louise	Newlyn
p	WD149	Alicia	Visitor
p	Ex SS272	Alison	Ex Plymouth
p	LI535	Alk II	Torquay
p	PZ810	Alvic	Newlyn
p	PZ1	Amanda J (Ex PZ9)	Penzance
p	FH664	Amethyst	Falmouth
p	SS261	Ammo	St Ives
p	Ex PH491	Amoco	Ex Plymouth
p	GU116	Amy Blue	Visitor
p	PW37	Amy O	Padstow

p	E495	Amy-R Ex Sophie/Ladram	Brixham
p	PZ44	Amy Rose	Coverack
p	Ex PH167	Anderton Lady	Plymouth
p	FY528	Andoray of Looe	Fowey
p	BM28	Angel Emiel	Brixham
p	SM271	Angelena	Exmouth
p	SE5	Anglo Dawn 11	Salcombe
p	BM510	Angus Rose	Brixham
p	FY537	Anjo	Looe
p	SE14	Ann	Salcombe
p	BD9	Anna	Appledore
p	PZ146	Anna Catherine	Cape Cornwall
p	SS262	Anna Maria (Girl)	Hayle
p	PZ80	Anna Rosa	Porthoustock
p	PZ197	Annaliese	Newlyn
p	Ex PZ1184	Anne Louise	Newlyn
p	PE477	Anthon	Plymouth
p	PZ331	Anthony Stevenson	Newlyn
	SS702	Antigri	Newlyn
p	Ex FH667	Antoinette	Porthoustock
p	FY96	Aquamanda	Fowey
p	FY324	Aquila	Mevagissey
p	PD220	Aquila	Visitor
p	PZ580	Aquilla	Mousehole
p	Ex FY41	Ar Tom	Looe (Ex Polperro)
p	E44	Arandora Star	River Tamar
p	Ex BM247	Arcomine	Ex Brixham
p	BD282	Argo	Appledore
p	FY814	Arrant	Looe
p	SE156	Artful Dodger III	Salcombe
p	SS8	Asper	St Ives
p	FY830	Atlantis	Looe
p	SC17	Atlantis	Scilly

ALPHABETICAL INDEX

p	BM499	Atlantis II	Teignmouth
p	E534	Attitude	Exmouth
p	SS52	Aurora	Newlyn
p	PE820	Avon Valley	St Mawes
p	PZ462	Aylishia	Porthallow
p	Ex TT254	Bain Hope	Clovelly
p	LO540	Banana Split	Porthoustock
p	IH180	Band of Hope	Newquay
p	E127	Barbara Jean	Beer
p	E18	Barbara Mae	Seaton
p	PH989	Barbican Lady	Plymouth
p	PH990	Barbican Maid	Newlyn (Ex Plymouth)
p	BM361	Barentszee	Plymouth
p	PZ490	Barry Ann	Sennen Cove
p	PZ99	Basil St Cl Stevenson	Newlyn
p	PZ527	Bass Boy	Church Cove
p	E508	Becci of Ladram	Exmouth
p	Ex E271	Bee J	Ex Beer
p	Ex PZ957	Bee-Jay	Newlyn
p	Ex FY473	Bekidil	Exmouth
p	FY846	Bella Margaret(Ex Pyscador)	Mevagissey
p	SS266	Belle Bettina	St Ives
p	PH587	Belle Etoile	Plymouth
p	FY661	Bellerophon	Ex Looe
p	WK3	Ben Loyal	Newlyn
p	PZ645	Ben My Chree	Newlyn
p	PE310	Ben Thomas	Fowey
p	FH623	Benediction	Portloe
p	PW1	Berlewen	Padstow
p	SS150	Bethany	Beer (Ex Teignmouth)
p	WH111	Bethany J	Padstow
p	FY852	Bethie Ann	Charlestown
p	E535	Betty-G (Ex NN716)	Exmouth
p	E487	Betty's Boys	Seaton
p	FH58	Billeric	Falmouth

p	PZ532	Billy Rowney	Newlyn
p	FY864	Black Pearl	Mevagissey
p	FY527	Blejan Eyhre	Newlyn
	FH683	Blithe Spirit	Ex Falmouth
p	BCK160	Blue Angel	Brixham
p	KY1001	Blue Diamond (Ex Charisma)	Newlyn
p	Ex PZ5	Blue Fin	Newlyn
p	PW460	Blue Fox	Padstow
p	E249	Blue Lady	Beer
p	FY399	Blue Marlin	Fowey
p	Ex FH209	Blue Minstrel	Falmouth
p	SE10	Blue Plover	St Ives
p	WH115	Boa Pescador	Porthleven
p	FH691	Bob Winnie	Cadgwith
p	FH322	Bobbie Dee II	River Fal
p	DH89	Bobolink	Dartmouth
p	BD292	Bombay	Clovelly
p	BM367	Bon Accord	Looe
p	PW470	Bon Amy	Padstow
p	SS711	Bonito	Falmouth
p	Ex PZ126	Bonnie	Mousehole
p	PW132	Boscastle Belle	Padstow
p	PW289	Boscastle Peganina	Boscastle
p	PH122	Bosloe	Plymouth
p	Ex PZ317	Bounders II	Newlyn
p	PH5587	Bounty	Plymouth
p	PZ302	Boy Adam	St Ives
p	SC168	Boy Adam	Scilly
	PZ43	Boy Andrew (Now Enigma)	Ex St Ives
p	FH597	Boy Brad	Porthoustock
p	WH578	Boy Brax (Ex Amro)	St Ives
p	SS276	Boy Chris	Newlyn
p	SS717	Boy Daniel	St Ives
p	SS189	Boy Darren	Padstow
p	SS699	Boy Dylan	Hayle

ALPHABETICAL INDEX

p	PZ379	Boy Harvey	Hayle
p	FH625	Boy Jack II	Plymouth
p	SC50	Boy Jan (Ex Zephyr)	Newlyn
p	FY588	Boy Joe II	Mevagissey
p	PW235	Boy John II	Port Isaac
p	TH165	Boy Karl	Teignmouth
p	BD76	Boy Lee	Bideford
p	SS671	Boy Louis	Porthleven
p	PZ699	Boy Matt	Sennen Cove
p	BM55	Boy Peter Now Kryst-le-Kay	Brixham Ex Helford R
p	BM40	Boy Philip	Torquay
p	PZ764	Boy Robert (Ex E Kathleen)	St Ives
p	TO41	Boy Ryan	St Ives
p	HL125	Boy Scott (Ex Chatterbox)	Plymouth
p	Ex SH127	Boy Steven	Padstow
p	FY764	Boy William	Fowey
p	FY838	Boys Own 2	Polperro
p	OB89	Braveheart	Falmouth
p	PH254	Brenda C	Plymouth
p	OB324	Bridie May	Hayle
p	SS665	Brissons	St Ives
p	FY71	Britannia II	Mevagissey
p	FH508	Britannia IV	Newlyn
p	DH141	Britannia of Beesands	Dartmouth
p	FH121	Britannia V	Newlyn
p	Ex FH145	Broadsword of Mylor	Maldon (Ex Falmouth)
p	PH58	Bruno of Sutton	Bideford
p	PZ290	Bryan D Stevenson	Newlyn
p	FY88	Buccaneer	Mevagissey
p	R84	Bumble B	Brixham
	Ex PZ346	Bumble B II	Ex Newlyn
p	SE154	Bung	Salcombe
p	FY162	Bunowen	Mevagissey
p	PZ584	Butts	Newlyn
p	FY578	C.H.E.A	Mevagissey

p	PZ1201	Cachalot	St Ives
p	SS54	Caliope	St Ives
p	Ex FY859	Callisto	Mevagissey
p	Ex FY773	Cara Mor	Teignmouth
	BM75	Carefree	Ex Brixham
p	PZ715	Cares Lel	Mevagissey
p	BM23	Carhelmar	Brixham
p	FH89	Cariad	Falmouth
p	NN257	Carina	Brixham
p	FR951	Carisanne II	Visitor
	BE13	Carla Jane	Ex Bideford
p	PH12	Carla May	Plymouth
p	FY847	Carlee	Looe
p	WK799	Carly Anne	Plymouth
p	PZ620	Carol & David	Penberth
p	WY379	Carol H	Newlyn
p	SE322	Carpe Diem	Mevagissey
p	Ex BRD222	Carrie Jane	Ex Looe
p	SS142	Carrie-Ann Lady	Plymouth
p	DH388	Cassius J	Padstow
p	BM282	Catear	Brixham
p	PZ32	Cathryn	Newlyn
p	Ex PH431	Cavio-Tan	Ex Plymouth
	Ex FY835	Cawte 1	Ex Mevagissey
p	FY614	Cazadora	Polperro
p	K1126	Ceol Na Mar (Ex Sara Jayne)	Appledore
p	UL2	Celestial Dawn	Falmouth
p	PZ557	Celtic Breeze	Hayle
p	PZ459	Celtic Lass (Ex Porthleven)	Falmouth
p	PW9	Celtic Mor	Padstow
p	CO365	Celtic Pride	Looe
p	PZ1200	Celtic Sunrise	Mullion
p	BM100	Centaur Now Cheryl ofLadram	Plymouth
p	Ex SC77	Ceres	Ex Looe

ALPHABETICAL INDEX

p	PZ184	Ceres	Newlyn
p	BD279	Ceri-Lee	Clovelly
p	BD1	Cerulean	Appledore
p	TO50	Cesca (Ex FR1 Accord)	Newlyn
p	PH5568	Challenge	River Yealm
p	PZ12	Chancer	Newlyn
p	SM799	Charella of Shoreham	Looe
p	BA45	Charisma	Padstow
p	SS11	Charisma	St Ives
p	SU515	Charity & Liberty	Looe
p	WH26	Charjon	Seaton
p	PW362	Charlotta	Mevagissey
p	SE18	Charlotte Ann	Salcombe
p	PZ756	Charlotte Louise II	Newlyn
p	FY777	Charltown	Charlestown
p	FY156	Charm	Mevagissey
p	HL125	Chatterbox (Now Boy Scott)	Plymouth
p	PW432	Che Sara Sara	Newquay
p	PH571	Cheryl Diana (Ex Fiona Grace)	Plymouth
p	BM100	Cheryl of Ladram (Ex Centaur)	Plymouth
p	PZ82	Chicadee	Newlyn
p	Ex PZ101	Children's Friend	Newlyn
p	PH277	Chiltern Boy	Plymouth
p	SS704	Chloe Estelle	Hayle
p	PZ1186	Chloet	Newlyn
p	NN95	Chrissann	Porthleven
p	FD100	Christina	Brixham
p	FY19	Christine	Mevagissey
p	Ex BM485	Christinie	Brixham
p	Ex WY788	Christy G	Salcombe
p	PZ425	CKS	Newlyn
p	PZ91	Clair	Sennen Cove
p	R39	Claire Louise	Brixham

p	SE150	Claire Louise	Salcombe
p	M126	Clairvoyant	Helford River
p	KY81	Comely II	Mevagissey
p	PH160	Compass Rose	Plymouth
p	M78	Compass Rose II	Ilfracombe
p	Ex PZ105	Constant	Newlyn
p	BM484	Constant Friend	Brixham
p	FY823	Conway	Mevagissey
p	Ex FY229	Coral	Hayle
p	FY167	Coral Reef	Porthleven
p	SC3	Coriana	Hayle
p	PZ4	Cormoran	Marazion
p	SS1	Cornish Crest	St Ives
p	PW32	Cornish Gem	Plymouth
p	FH636	Cornish Gem	Plymouth
p	PZ339	Cornish Lass	Newlyn
p	FH702	Cornish Lass	Falmouth
p	FY866	Cornish Lass III (Ex BF267)	Fowey
p	FH717	Cornish Lass IV	Coverack
p	Ex FY662	Cornish Maid	Looe
p	FY242	Cornish Maid of Looe	Downderry
p	PZ512	Cornishman	Newlyn
p	FY868	Cornishman	Mevagissey
p	INS292	Courageous III	Visitor
p	Ex FY118	Cousin Jack	Looe
p	Ex PZ748	Cousin Jack	Ex Falmouth
p	FH496	Craggan	Brixham
p	FY95	Cristal waters (Ex Virgo Lady)	Plymouth
	DH71	Crusader of Kingswear	Dartmouth
p	SE35	Crustacean	Salcombe
p	SS118	Crystal Sea	Newlyn
p	PZ585	Curlew	Penberth
p	Ex SC70	Curlew	Scilly

p	HL1059	Cyclone	Newquay
p	E30	Cygnet	Ex Beer (in Scotland)
p	PZ734	Cynth	Scilly
p	PZ663	Cynthia	St Ives
p	SS136	Cynthia	Newlyn
p	Ex PH962	D J	Ex Plymouth
p	Ex WA254	Dabar	Fowey (Ex Plymouth)
p	PZ1172	Daisy Christianne	Newlyn
p	DH133	Damsel Fly	Dartmouth
p	BM478	Danielle	Brixham
p	M8	Danmark	Penzance
p	PZ1197	Danni Rose	St Ives
p	SS226	Daphne Rose	Penberth
p	PH316	Darter	Plymouth
p	WH461	Davrik II	Salcombe
p	DH77	Dawn	Torcross
p	P940	Dawn Raider	Polperro
p	DH86	Dawn Raider	Torcross
p	PW333	Daymer Bay	Padstow
p	BM234	De Vrouw Marie	Brixham
p	BM5	Dee-J (Ex Stormchild)	Brixham (Ex Polperro)
p	FY848	Defiant	Mevagissey
p	DH405	Deejay	Dartmouth
p	PD959	Demares	Visitor
p	TH155	Deepcore	Teignmouth
p	FY53	Demelza	Mevagissey
p	FY841	Demper	Mevagissey
p	FY290	Deu Kerens (Yawl)	Looe
p	Ex INS154	Diadem	Ex Padstow
p	SS7	Diana	Sennen Cove
p	DH394	Dianne T	Dartmouth
p	Ex E274	Dickie Bird II	Seaton
p	M560	Dignity	Plymouth
p	PW240	Diligence	Padstow
p	SS687	Dillan	Padstow

p	Ex SS19	Dino	Helford River
p	PH381	Dionne	Newquay
p	PW459	Dire Straits	Plymouth
p	FY303	Dispatcher	Looe
p	TH121	Diverse	Teignmouth
	Ex BE3	Dolphin	Ex Barnstaple
p	LL271	Dolphin	Plymouth
	SE324	Dolphin	Ex Salcombe
p	FH609	Domar	Falmouth
p	CL22	Don Valley	Plymouth
	PW439	Donna Marie	Ex Mevagissey
p	PW453	Doo Da Day	Mousehole
p	WH97	Dragun-An-Moar	St Ives
p	NN147	Duchess	Appledore
p	PH575	Duet	River Tamar
p	SE25	Dunlin	Salcombe
p	DH384	DVFG	Dartmouth
p	PW437	Early Bird	Bude
p	SS50	Early Dawn	St Ives
p	BM176	Ebonnie	Brixham
p	DH397	Ebony Rose	Dartmouth
p	UL178	Eclipse	Newquay
p	PZ1174	Edward J (Ex Ennis Lady)	Boscastle
p	SS718	Eel-Avum (Ex Three Boys)	Penzance
	FH638	Ela-J	Ex Falmouth
p	PW95	Eleanor Roget	Padstow
p	BS472	Elise (Ex Gwenfaen)	Brixham
p	SS92	Elishia	Newlyn
p	SE334	Elizabeth	Salcombe
p	PZ291	Elizabeth A Webster	Newlyn
p	PZ293	Elizabeth Caroline	Newlyn
p	FH289	Elizabeth Madeline	Newquay
p	PZ100	Elizabeth N	Newlyn
p	FY24	Ella	Looe
p	SS697	Elle V	Hayle

p	PZ1193	Ellie Mae	Newlyn
p	DH392	Elm	Dartmouth
p	Ex E53	Elsie	Exmouth
p	TH419	Emaley	Torquay
p	FY174	Emblem	Gorran Haven
p	BM498	Emerald	Torquay
p	SC35	Emerald Dawn	Scilly
p	PZ34	Emily	Newlyn
p	SE330	Emily Ann	Salcombe
p	E458	Emily B	Portreath
p	E123	Emily J	Exmouth
p	BCK222	Emily Jane	Visitor
p	LT70	Emily Rose	Dartmouth
p	SE101	Emma Jane	Salcombe
p	Ex SE8	Emma Jo	Hope Cove
p	Ex PW11	Emma Kate (Ex Padstow)	Teignmouth
p	PW10	Emma Kate ll	Padstow
p	PZ764	Emma Kathleen Now Boy Robert	St Ives
p	PH5557	Emma Louise	Plymouth
p	FH416	Emma May	Looe
p	SC164	Emma Rose	Padstow
p	ExPE524	Endeavour	Plymouth
p	PZ50	Ennis Lady (Ex Kingfisher)	Porthleven
p	P29	Equinox	Ex Mevagissey
p	FY127	Erin	Looe
p	PW392	Erindors	Padstow
p	E92	Esme	Exmouth
p	Ex BD10	Estrel Do Mar	Appledore
p	SO958	Eternal Dawn	Visitor
p	WH696	Etoile des Ondes	Teignmouth
p	E6	Evelyn	Ex Brixham (Wales)
p	FH280	Evening Star	Coverack
p	Ex J219	Evert Marutje	River Tamar
p	DH17	Excel	Dartmouth
p	PZ513	Excellent	Newlyn

p	H105	Excelsior	Plymouth
p	TH21	Eyecatcher	Lynmouth
p	PH5590	Fair Trade (Ex LI 133)	Plymouth
p	FY822	Fair Wind	Polperro
p	SC84	Faith	Teignmouth
p	SU513	Faith	Polperro
p	PZ39	Father Bob	Penberth
	DH26	Felicity	Ex Dartmouth
p	LT976	Fenlander	Port Isaac
p	PZ542	Filadelfia	Newlyn
p	PW440	Finnish Girl	Falmouth
p	FY853	Finn-Lou	Looe
p	SS194	Fiona & Tracy	St Ives
p	PH571	Fiona Grace (Ex Chery Diana)	River Tamar
p	PW160	Fiona Mary	Brixham
p	FH730	Fiona Starr	Falmouth
p	Ex SC142	First Swallow	Scilly
p	J86	Fleur de France	Visitor
p	KY115	Flourish	Exmouth
p	PZ574	Flowing Tide	Mullion
p	FH106	Flying Breeze	Coverack
p	Ex PH299	Flying Freckles	Plymouth
	PW469	For a Few Dollars More	Hayle
p	SC19	Forget-Me-Not	Newlyn
p	SS685	Fou de Bassin	Hayle
p	FH57	Foxy lady	Porthoustock
p	Ex M313	Foxy Lady	Ex Plymouth
p	PZ1	Fran Beth	Newlyn
p	Ex FY238	Frances	Ex Mevagissey
p	FH714	Frances B	Falmouth
	E167	Frances Jane	Lyme Regis
p	Ex J217	Frances of Ladram (Ex PZ100)	Ex Plymouth
p	PZ437	Frances Rose	Newlyn
p	E457	Francis B	Sidmouth
p	PH99	Franjo A	Plymouth

p	PW446	Free Spirit	Port Isaac
p	SD383	Freedom	River Tamar
p	DH97	Full Monty	Dartmouth
p	FY4	Fulmar	Gorran Haven
p	PZ601	Fulmar	Cadgwith
p	FY97	Galatea	Looe
p	SE75	Galloper	Salcombe
p	SC177	Gallos	Scilly
p	FH76	Galwad-Y-Mor	Mevagissey
p	FH246	Gamgy Lady	Falmouth
p	Ex PH207	Gammarus	Plymouth
p	E4	Garn	Budleigh Salterton
p	Ex PZ643	Gary-M	Newlyn
p	PZ536	Gazelle	Penberth
p	BM140	Geeske	Brixham
p	BD18	Gemini	Porthleven
p	PZ1202	Gemini Two	St Ives
p	PZ40	Gemma	St Ives
p	Ex FH130	Gemma Claire	Scilly
p	SE58	George Edwin	Salcombe
p	BM298	George Johannes	Newlyn
p	PW449	George-D	Dartmouth
p	Ex FY12	Georgie Girl	Newlyn
p	Ex BD109	Georgina	Ex Ilfracombe
p	TN38	Georg'Lou N (Ex PZ87)	Visitor
p	TH169	Gerry Ann	Looe
p	TH257	Gerry Ann C	Brixham
p	BM67	Gina Louise	Brixham
p	DR166	Gipsy King	Padstow
p	Ex TH12	Gipsy Mermaid	Plymouth
p	FY755	Girl Amanda	Looe
p	FY824	Girl Bryher	Newlyn
p	E444	Girl Debra	Brixham
p	HL1061	Girl Emma	Plymouth

p	Ex PZ54	Girl Frances	Lizard
p	PH9	Girl Gillian	Falmouth
p	FH468	Girl Jan	Porthoustock
p	SD80	Girl Jane	Polperro
p	Ex SE9	Girl Jean II	Hope Cove
p	SS104	Girl Karen	St Ives
p	PZ85	Girl Kim	Newlyn
p	LO59	Girl Linda	Hayle
p	PZ6	Girl Pamela	Newlyn
p	PZ57	Girl Patricia	Newlyn
p	FH293	Girl Pauline	Porthoustock
p	Ex PZ639	Girl Pearl	Porthleven
p	PZ353	Girl Penny	Newlyn
p	FH598	Girl Rachael	Falmouth
p	PW77	Girl Rachel	Padstow
p	TH117	Girl Rona	Teignmouth
p	AH101	Girl Soo	Plymouth
p	PZ1187	Girl Stella	Hayle
p	TH260	Girl Tracey	Torquay
p	LT1015	Glad Rags	Fowey
	BD128	Gladys Jean	Ex Bideford
p	PZ777	Gloria	Sennen Cove
p	PZ903	Go-For-It	Newlyn
p	FH206	Golden Fleece	Falmouth
p	PZ1198	Golden Fleece	Porthleven
p	FR59	Golden Gain V	Visitor
p	PZ63	Golden Harvest	Newlyn
p	Ex YH5	Golden Harvest	Exmouth
p	TH288	Golden Lancer	Padstow
p	TO48	Good Fortune	Portreath
p	E523	Good Life	Seaton
p	ExPZ8	Grace	Newlyn
p	B80	Green Isles II	Ilfracombe
p	FY827	Greta's Girl (Ex Cornish Lass II)	Ex Fowey

p	TH52	Grey Dawn	Plymouth
p	PZ540	Grey Seal	Penberth
p	Ex J347	Grietje	Brixham (Ex Plymouth)
p	SS3	Guide Me	Mevagissey
p	PW377	Guiding Light	Ex Looe
p	NN722	Guiding Light II (Ex Alena)	Looe
p	PZ61	Guiding Star	Newlyn
p	SE122	Guillemot	Salcombe
p	E460	Gus	Sidmouth
p	BM1	Guyona	Brixham
p	PH586	Gwalarn	Plymouth
p	PW461	Gwendra	Padstow
p	BS472	Gwenfaen (Now Elise)	Brixham
p	SS21	Hanna G	St Ives
p	BM2	Hannah D	Brixham
p	PH5583	Hannah Jack	Plymouth
p	BM218	Haringvliet	Brixham
p	BM51	Harm Johannes	Brixham
p	PH5573	Harrier	Plymouth
p	BM487	Hartley	Looe
p	TT177	Harvest Reaper	Visitor
p	PZ329	Harvest Reaper	Newlyn
p	FH198	Harvester (Now Bridlington)	Ex Falmouth
p	BM127	Harvester (Ex E496)	Brixham
p	FH723	Harvester II	Falmouth
p	SS151	Hawk	Mousehole
p	Ex BW40	Hazy Dawn	Brixham
p	E14	Heart of Oak	Plymouth
p	Ex SC53	Heather Ann	Ex Padstow
p	FY126	Heather Anne	Mevagissey
p	DH76	Heatseeker	Dartmouth
p	PH5562	Helcon	Appledore
p	BM258	Helen Claire	Brixham
p	PW429	Helen Claire II	Port Isaac

p	FY865	Helen Clare	Charlestown
p	PW412	Helen Jane	Newquay
p	PW124	Helen Jane II	Padstow
p	BM76	Hell-of-a-Dear	Teignmouth
p	PZ682	Helona	Newlyn
p	TH19	Henry	Teignmouth
p	Ex RX155	Hercules	Plymouth
p	PZ654	Hicca	Penberth
p	FY531	Hickie	Fowey
p	SS700	Highlander of Hayle	Newlyn
p	FH705	Hobbit	Falmouth
p	Ex SS59	Honey Bee	Newlyn
p	PD905	Honeybourne III	Visitor
p	PH477	Hooker	Clovelly
p	SU514	Hope	Polperro
p	SS65	Hope	Newlyn
p	Ex TH64	Hopkins I	Teignmouth
p	SS134	Huers	Newlyn
p	FY424	Huntress	Mevagissey
p	SC66	Hustler	Dartmouth
p	FY292	Ibis	Mevagissey
p	Ex FY519	Ibis	River Tamar
p	FH93	Ida May	Church Cove
p	Ex PZ233	I'll Try	Helford River
p	DH46	Independent	Brixham
p	FY46	Innisfallen (Ex Plymouth)	Newlyn
p	Ex CA44	Innisfree	Ex Paignton
p	TO40	Intuition	Newlyn
p	FY367	Investor (Ex Ocean Venture)	Mevagissey
p	FH23	Iona	Portscatho
p	D592	Irish Rose	Visitor
p	PH564	Isabella	Plymouth
	FH398	Isabelle	Ex Falmouth
p	Ex PZ9	Isabelle	Porthleven

ALPHABETICAL INDEX

p	SC27	Isis	Fowey
p	CN119	Islander	Mousehole
p	FY296	Islander	Polperro
p	SS242	Ivy	Newlyn
p	GY341	Iysha	Visitor
p	Ex FY832	Izaak	Ex Mevagissey
p	BM503	J C K	Brixham
p	SY16	Jacamar II	Visitor
p	BE85	Jack	Appledore
p	PZ779	Jack-Anny	Newlyn
p	PZ495	Jackie Marie	Mevagissey
p	BM248	Jacky J	Brixham
p	BM77	Jacoba	Brixham
p	BM208	Jacomina	Brixham
p	PW474	Jacqueline	Padstow
p	PZ192	Jacqueline	Newlyn
p	PZ695	Jade	Hayle
p	Ex SS667	Jae	Looe
p	PZ78	James R H Stevenson	Newlyn
p	Ex PW96	Jan B	Lynmouth
p	SS144	Janet Anne	St Ives
p	PW20	Janice Mary	Padstow
p	PZ999	Jannie en Klaas	Newlyn
p	FH75	Jasmine	Portloe
p	Ex BA816	Jaycee	Ex Looe
p	PW150	Jean Howard	Appledore
p	BRD92	J-Anne	Newlyn
p	B953	J-Lee	Newlyn
p	SS170	Jen	St Ives
p	FH200	Jen Lou II	Porthoustock
	PZ20	Jenny	Ex Newlyn
p	FY545	Jenny James	Gorran Haven
p	Ex PZ1177	Jess	Sennen Cove
p	FY807	Jessica Grace	Fowey

p	PZ1189	Jessica Ione	Teignmouth
p	PH344	Jessie Lou	Plymouth
p	FY837	Jimini K	Mevagissey
p	NN137	Joanna	Looe
p	BM265	Joanna C	Brixham
p	DH300	Jodie Ann	Teignmouth
p	Ex TH22	Jodie V	Seaton
p	PZ689	John Louise	Newlyn
p	SS284	John Wesley	Looe
p	DH183	Joint Venture	Dartmouth
	FY64	Jolie Brise	Ex Mevagissey
p	SS112	Jonathan Seagull	St Ives
p	Ex PH221	Jontine	Plymouth
p	BM508	Jose Jacqualine	Brixham
p	E225	Joy of Ladram (Ex J225)	Plymouth
p	Ex E496	Joy of Ladram (Now Harvester)	Brixham
p	Ex SS221	Julia Nadine	St Ives
	E227	Julie	Ex Exmouth
p	PW81	Julie Girl	Helford River
p	FH672	Kaisa Mari (Ex Looe)	Teignmouth
p	WH584	Kaluger	Brixham
p	SC163	Kameruka	Scilly
p	FY566	Karan	St Ives
p	SC170	Karenza	Scilly
p	FH88	Karenza Jayne	Helford River
p	E20	Karli-N	River Tamar
p	BM517	Kasey Marie	Brixham
p	PH5561	Katherine M	Plymouth
p	SU511	Kathleen	Looe
p	FH629	Kathryn Louise II	The Lizard
p	PZ87	Katie Claire (Ex FD407)	Newlyn
p	FY180	Katie Lil	Portloe
p	FY834	Katie's Pride	Charlestown
p	SE40	Katrina	Brixham

p	PH530	Katrina	Plymouth
p	CS295	Katy	Gorran Haven
p	FY839	Katytu	Looe
p	TH424	Kay-Larie (Ex Wally)	Teignmouth
p	OB454	Kelley Marena	Brixham
p	SS25	Kelly Girl	St Ives
p	PH271	Kelly J	Plymouth
p	PZ480	Kelyn Mor	Newquay
p	FH258	Kendore (Ex Falmouth)	Brixham
p	FH613	Kerany	Porthoustock
p	SS695	Keriolet	Padstow
p	J235	Kerloch	Visitor
p	FY63	Kerry Jane	Mevagissey
p	FY115	Kessenyans	Looe
p	BCK81	Kestrel	Visitor
p	SE15	Kevi-Tor-Ru	Salcombe
p	E15	Kimberley	Exmouth
p	FH715	Kimberley Jo	Falmouth
p	BK524	Kindly Light D	Helford River
p	Ex BE83	Kingfisher	Ex Lynmouth
p	BE83	Kingfisher	Ilfracombe
	DH110	Kingfisher	Ex Dartmouth
p	FH529	Kingfisher II	Cadgwith
p	FY17	Kingfisher of Looe	Mevagissey
p	BA87	King Challenger	Visitor
p	PH574	Kinsman	Plymouth
p	Ex SS295	Kiskey	Sennen Cove
p	Ex PH98	Kittiwake	Plymouth
p	Ex FD508	Kon Tiki	Newlyn
p	FH187	Kon-Tiki	Helford River
p	LT535	Korenbloem	Brixham
p	BM55	Kryst-le-Kay (Ex Boy Peter)	Brixham (Ex Helford)
p	BE29	K-Sands	Bideford
p	PH11	KSH	River Tamar

p	PW201	La Conquete	Brixham
p	PH588	La Coquet	Falmouth
p	BM177	La Creole	Brixham
p	J612	La Vagabonde	Teignmouth
p	SS96	Lady Anne	St Ives
p	Ex FY456	Lady Betty II	Padstow
p	P965	Lady Claire	Newlyn
p	PW287	Lady Di	Portreath
p	FH214	Lady Hamilton	Helford River
p	Ex PH961	Lady Jane (LK780 Merlin)	Ex Plymouth
p	SS681	Lady Joan	St Ives
p	BM128	Lady Lou	Brixham
p	BM476	Lady Maggie	Salcombe
p	PE888	Lady Matilda	Helford River
p	BM7	Lady Maureen (Ex J276))	Brixham
p	BM2000	Lady T Emiel	Brixham
p	PZ683	Lafrowda	Portreath
p	SY36	Lamorna	Padstow
p	SS28	Lamorna	Newlyn
p	Ex PH48	Lancer	Plymouth
p	ExPH5575	Lark	Plymouth
p	IH68	Laura Anne	River Yealm
p	PZ72	Lauran	Newlyn
p	FY836	Lauren Kate	Mevagissey
p	PZ453	Laurie Jean	Scilly
p	PW36	Le Loustic (Ex R472)	Padstow
p	PZ98	Leader	Newlyn
p	PZ212	Lee-Am	Mousehole
p	PW455	Lenny P (Ex Fowey)	Port Gaverne
p	FY43	Lenten Rose	Mevagissey
p	SE328	Leo 2	Salcombe
p	TH287	Leonara	Bigbury on Sea
p	Ex SC60	Leonora	Mevagissey

p	BM166	Lerina	Brixham
p	BM87	Les Mercenaires	Brixham
p	FY269	Levan-Mor of Looe	Looe
p	FH485	Leviathan	Falmouth
p	BM11	Liam John II	Torquay
p	Ex FH151	Liberator	Ex Portholland
p	FY431	Liberty	Mevagissey
p	PE487	Libra Lass	Brixham
p	E43	Lillie May	Beer
p	PZ457	Lily	Mousehole
p	PW197	Lily May	Bude
p	PW456	Lily May II	Bude
p	FY781	Linda B	Newlyn
p	Ex PW410	Linda J	Bude
p	ExPH5584	Lindora (Atalanta Yacht)	Ex River Tamar
p	Ex FY382	Lindy Lou	Falmouth
p	SM77	Lindy Lou	Clovelly
p	PZ395	Lisa	Newlyn
p	Ex RX39	Lisa Ann	Ex Plymouth
p	PZ476	Lisa Jacquie Stevenson	Newlyn
p	BM479	Lisa K	Brixham
p	PH598	Lisa Leanne	Plymouth
p	RX369	Lisana (Ex Bethan Louise)	Teignmouth
p	FY302	Lisanne of Looe	Looe
p	FY765	Little Anne	Mevagissey
p	Ex BM98	Little Boy Blue	Ex Paignton
p	BM98	Little Boy Blue	Paignton
p	SS80	Little Christina	St Ives
p	SE20	Little Emiel	Brixham
p	FY29	Little Fisher	Mevagissey
p	E456	Little Gem	Brixham
p	Ex PZ758	Little Halcyon	Mousehole
p	FY23	Little Pearl	Newlyn

p	PW60	Little Pearl	Salcombe
p	PZ890	Little Waters	Newlyn
p	FY345	Liver Bird	Mevagissey
p	FH693	Lizy	Mevagissey
p	BM188	Lloyd Tyler	Brixham
	PZ130	Lone Wolf	Ex Newlyn
p	PZ48	Lorraine Ruth	Salcombe
p	SC169	Lorraine Ruth	Scilly
p	E74	Louise	Exmouth
p	SC2	Lowena	Scilly
p	PZ47	Lowena-Mor	Newlyn
p	Ex PZ167	Lowenek	Mullion Cove
p	TO49	Lower Lights	Falmouth
p	PZ30	Loyal Partner	Newquay
p	Ex DH82	Lucky Dip	Salcombe
p	M1141	Lucy	Brixham
p	FY843	Lucy B	Mevagissey
p	E449	Lucy M	Exmouth
p	FY239	Lucy Marianna	Helford River
p	FY66	Lucy Too	Looe
p	PZ439	Lugi	Newlyn
p	Ex RX76	Lumbering Elephant	Exmouth
	BD2	Lundy Star	Bideford
p	Ex BD220	Lundy Star	Bideford
p	SS713	Lyonesse	Hayle
p	FY555	Lyonesse	Mevagissey
p	PZ478	Lyonesse of Cape	Cape Cornwall
p	PW182	M C B	Polperro
p	PZ632	Macareux (Ex Exmouth)	Ilfracombe
p	BM241	Magdalena	Brixham
p	DH60	Maggie Marie	Dartmouth
p	BM492	Maggie (Ex Dartmouth)	River Yealm
p	BM511	Magnum	Newlyn
p	DH20	Magnum	Dartmouth

p	FY138	Ma-Gondole	Padstow
p	PZ1181	Maid Donna	Porthleven
p	SS673	Maid Mel	Hayle
p	FY195	Maid of Boddinick	Padstow
p	SC167	Maiden Bower	Scilly
p	FY400	Mako	Mevagissey
	Ex PW310	Mako III	Ex Padstow
p	PW431	Mako of Bude	Bude
p	BM147	Malkerry	Brixham
p	BD257	Mallagar	Brixham
p	BM66	Mar Rose	Brixham
p	SS149	Maranatha	Scilly
p	SC175	Marauder	Scilly
p	GU74	Maraunders (Ex BM192)	Alderney (Ex Brixham)
p	R159	Maret	Looe
p	LT526	Mareverma	Brixham
p	TH20	Margaret	Teignmouth
p	E88	Margaret of Ladram(Ex J588)	Plymouth
p	Ex E476	Margh An Mor	Exmouth
p	FH669	Maria 2	Falmouth
p	FH109	Maria Q	Mevagissey
p	PZ295	Marie Claire	Newlyn
p	BM169	Marilyn Jayne	Brixham
p	BM190	Marina	Brixham
p	Ex SS224	Mariner	St Ives
p	FY569	Marion	Looe
p	PZ641	Mark & James	St Ives
p	BD296	Marlin	Ex Ilfracombe
	SC171	Marlin	Scilly
p	SS683	Marlin G	Hayle
	FH601	Marney Lunn	Ex Helford River
p	E217	Marta	Sidmouth
p	E256	Marth-D	Seaton
p	SE158	Martlett	Salcombe

p	BM482	Mary Anne	Brixham
p	YH299	Mary D	Port Isaac
p	FY811	Mary Eileen	Mevagissey
p	PZ575	Mary Frances	Falmouth
p	WD220	Mary Kate	Visitor
p	PZ477	Mary Rose	Porthoustock
p	PZ190	Mathew Harvey	Newlyn
p	TN36	Mattanja	Visitor
p	PH589	Maverick	Plymouth
p	PW228	Ma-Vie	Helford River
p	FY38	Maxine's Pride	Looe
	Ex SS47	May	Ex St Ives
p	DH8	Mayfly	Dartmouth
p	Ex FY173	May Queen	River Tamar
p	SE138	May Queen	Salcombe
p	Ex BD283	Melanie Anne	Bude
p	PZ179	Mer Breeze (Ex Polperro)	Newquay
p	SS85	Merlin	St Ives
p	LK780	Merlin (Ex Lady Jane)	Ex Plymouth
p	BD290	Mermaid	Clovelly
p	PH322	Metan	Plymouth
p	E520	Mia B	Exmouth
p	PZ436	Michael & David	Newlyn
	Ex BM158	Michelle Louisa	Ex Brixham
p	SS698	Midnight Express	St Ives
p	TH24	Midnight Sun	Plymouth
p	Ex FH176	Milly	Coverack
p	Ex CK181	Mini-Me (Ex Surf-Rider II)	Ex Looe
p	PZ124	Minnow	Hayle
p	SE333	Minstrel (Now Provider)	Salcombe
p	DH11	Miranda	Beesands
p	Ex BL31	Mischief	Dartmouth
p	OB146	Mistress III	Newquay

p	FH21	Misty Blue	Falmouth
p	PH326	Moby Dick	Teignmouth
p	WD87	Molly B	Visitor
p	DH62	Moonfleet	Salcombe
p	PH5586	Moonraker	River Tamar
p	FY523	Mordros	Mevagissey
p	FH12	Morel Margh	Falmouth
P	FY872	Morgellan	Mevagissey
p	Ex OB61	Morning Glory	Looe
p	PZ9	Morning Star (Ex PZ21)	Porthleven
p	FY15	Morvina	Mevagissey
p	Ex BM222	Mourne Lass	Brixham
p	PZ674	Mouzel Dawn	St Ives
p	PH5577	My Diane	Plymouth
p	PH572	My Girls	Polperro
p	E28	My Lady	Seaton
p	BM115	My Mikaela	Brixham
p	SS148	My Partner	Falmouth
p	Ex BM474	Mystere	Brixham
p	Ex FY768	Mystique II	Newquay (ExLooe)
p	PZ778	Naomi G	Clovelly
p	PZ482	Nampara	Hayle
p	FY602	Natalie	Looe
p	H1074	Natalie B	Visitor
p	Ex FY576	Natalie Clare	Falmouth
p	SC21	Nazarene	St Ives
p	PZ10	Nellie	Newlyn
p	CF1	Nemesis	Plymouth
p	BD69	Neptune	Clovelly
p	PH82	Neptune	Portwrinkle
p	SD201	Neptune	River Tamar
p	FY767	Neptune's Pride II	Looe

p	SS706	Nessie	Hayle
p	FH677	New Dawn	Falmouth
p	PH5585	New Dawn (Ex GU360)	Brixham
p	DH149	Newbrook	Dartmouth
p	Ex FH229	Newlek-Mor	Portreath
p	DH1	Nicky V	Dartmouth
p	Ex PW436	Nicola J	Padstow
p	BM491	Nicola Jayne	Brixham
p	Ex SS258	Nicola Marie	St Ives
p	SS126	Nikki Louise	Newlyn
p	DH390	Nil Desperandum	Dartmouth
p	BM44	Nipper	Brixham
p	BM489	Nirvana	Brixham
p	SS53	Norah-T	St Ives
p	FY226	Nor'Rocker	Falmouth
p	DH119	Northern Clipper	Dartmouth
p	Ex CS112	Northern Kiwi	Porthoustock
p	PH650	Northern Lass	Plymouth
p	YH320	Northern Lights	Newquay
p	FY583	Northern Star II	Polperro
p	SC16	Northern Star II	Scilly
p	SC25	Northwood	Looe
p	FY44	Norvik	Plymouth
p	CN187	Nova Spero	Newlyn
p	FY857	Ocean Blue	Looe
p	PZ775	Ocean Breeze	Newlyn
p	ExPH5579	Ocean Breeze	Ex Plymouth
p	FR317	Ocean Crest	Visitor
p	FR347	Ocean Dawn	Visitor
p	SY5	Ocean Harvest	Mevagissey
p	PD198	Ocean Harvest	Visitor
	BD97	Ocean Monarch	Ex Bude
p	FY26	Ocean Queen	Polperro
p	FR317	Ocean Quest	Fraserburgh

p	PZ41	Ocean Spray	Newlyn
p	FR894	Ocean Star	Visitor
p	WY36	Ocean Venture II (Now Investor FY367)	Ex Falmouth
p	BE9	October Morning	Lynmouth
p	SS689	Ohio	Polperro
p	FH2	Olga Annie	Falmouth
p	BD277	Olivier Belle	Ilfracombe
p	PH74	Onward	Falmouth
p	PZ768	Onward	Newlyn
p	Ex BM202	(Onze) Linquenda	Ex Brixham
p	PZ1188	Ophelia	Falmouth (Ex Newlyn)
p	Ex FD114	Ora et Labora	Ex Brixham
p	FY228	Orca (Ex Reefer)	Downderry
p	SS707	Orca	Hayle
p	PW364	Orcades II	Port Isaac
p	SS273	Orion	St Ives
p	HH76	Osprey	Newlyn
p	WK127	Osprey	Porthleven
p	SS17	Osprey	St Ives
p	BE6	Otter	Barnstaple
p	E25	Otter	Budleigh Salterton
p	PW100	Our Belle Ann	Port Isaac
p	LT1	Our Boy Andrew	Looe
p	FY221	Our Boys	Looe
p	Ex FY7	Our Daddy	Looe
p	E161	Our Endeavour	Plymouth
p	BM172	Our Johanna	Brixham
p	BD287	Our Josie Grace	Ilfracombe
	FY47	Our Liz	Ex St Ives
p	PH584	Our Louise	Ex Plymouth
p	PZ738	Our Margaret	St Ives
p	BM150	Our Maria	Brixham
p	BM27	Our Miranda	Brixham
p	Ex PZ403	Our Ocean Harvester	Ex Newlyn
p	DH135	Our Pammy	Dartmouth
p	Ex FY862	Our Sophie	Looe
p	IH23	Our Steph	Brixham
p	Ex FY141	Our Trio	Looe
p	BM342	Our Wendy	Torquay
p	BM264	Our Zoe Anne	Brixham
p	E513	Outcast	Seaton
p	SE46	Outsetter	Salcombe
p	DH92	P.W.S.	Torcross
p	GY165	Pacemaker	Ilfracombe
p	PW75	Palores	Polperro
p	PZ21	Pandorra III	Mousehole
p	FY860	Pania	Looe
p	FY369	Paravel	Looe
p	AB199	Pathfinder	Newquay
p	PZ125	Patrice	Mullion
p	FH55	Patrice II	Falmouth
p	PZ140	Paul Arran	St Ives
p	Ex FY362	Paula III	Looe
p	FH300	Paula Rose	Falmouth
p	PH245	Pauline J	Plymouth
p	BM24	Peace & Plenty III	Brixham
p	SE332	Peadar Elaine	Salcombe
p	PZ729	Pegasus	Newlyn
p	SC76	Pelican	Scilly
p	SE34	Pen Glas	Salcombe
p	PZ84	Pen Kernow	Cape Cornwall
p	PZ1183	Pendower	Newlyn
p	SC22	Penguin	Scilly
p	Ex PZ747	Penny Lynn	Penberth
p	Ex PZ211	Pet	Falmouth
p	FH690	Peter John II	Falmouth
p	SS138	Peter Pan	St Ives

ALPHABETICAL INDEX

p	PH5578	Petit Folie	Plymouth
p	Ex FY664	Petit Mickael	Fowey
p	TN37	Philomena	Newlyn
p	SE33	Phoenix	Salcombe
p	FY804	Phoenix	Looe
p	SS66	Phra-Nang	Hayle
p	TN39	Piedras	Visitor
p	Ex J535	Pieter	Ex Plymouth
p	Ex J192	Pieterje	Ex Plymouth
p	FY797	Pimpernel II	Mevagissey
p	YH1	Pioneer	Bideford
p	Ex PZ277	Pioneer	Hayle
p	SC41	Pioneer	Scilly
p	DH74	Pisces	Beesands
	PW105	Pisces II	Ex Port Isaac
p	PW13	Plover	Padstow
p	PZ770	Pol Pry II	Sennen Cove
p	Ex TH71	Polarlys	Teignmouth
p	SC172	Pontious	Scilly
p	Ex PZ883	Prevail	Newlyn
p	PZ260	Princess Diane	Porthleven
p	Ex FY562	Progress	Looe
p	FH442	Proper Job	Falmouth
p	FH722	Prophet	Falmouth
p	OB2	Prospect	Exmouth
p	WH264	Prospector	Newlyn
p	E533	Prosperity	Exmouth
p	E87	Provider	Appledore
p	SS225	Provider (Ex Minstrel)	St Ives
p	PZ550	Prue Esther II	Newlyn
p	FY278	Puffin	Mevagissey
	Ex FY617	Pyscador (Now Bella Margaret)	Mevagissey

p	PZ612	Rachel & Paul;	Newlyn
p	PZ1015	Rachel & Victoria	Plymouth
p	Ex PZ570	Rachel Cara	Cape Cornwall
p	BM192	Rachel Louise	Brixham
p	FY270	Radjel	Mevagissey
p	PH76	Raven	River Tamar
p	Ex SS670	Ray of Hope	Mousehole
p	SS268	Razorbill	Cadgwith
p	PZ800	Rebecca Ann	Newlyn
p	FY111	Red Vixen	Mevagissey
p	BM6	Reel One	Brixham
p	FH5	Regina Maris of Helford	Ex Helford River
p	DH88	Rejoice	Dartmouth
p	PZ475	Reliance	Porthleven
p	E519	Rene	Sidmouth
p	FY254	Renown	Mevagissey
p	LK37	Renown	Padstow
p	FY119	Resolute	Mevagissey
p	SC173	Resolution	Scilly
p	PZ1001	Resurgam	Newlyn
p	PZ520	Reward (Ex Harvest Home)	St Ives
p	SS173	Rhiannon Jane	Mevagissey
p	PH959	Richard Ann	Plymouth
p	PW463	Roams	Port Gaverne
p	SS23	Roannah (Ex YH800)	Newlyn
p	E22	Roanne	Exmouth
p	DH21	Rob Roy	Beesands
	TH84	Robert	Ex Mevagissey
p	TH135	Rock Hopper	Paignton
p	Ex SC4	Rockhopper	Scilly
p	FH686	Rose	Portscatho
p	PZ1209	Rose Bud	Newlyn
p	LT278	Rose Dawn	Ex Mevagissey

p	PZ194	Roseland	Newlyn
p	PD313	Rosemount	Visitor
p	PZ1024	Ros-Na-Riogh	Newlyn
p	E521	Rowella of Ladram	Exmouth
p	SC73	Rowen-Mor(Ex Pioneer II)	Scilly
p	FH704	Reuben Luke	Helford River
p	FY829	Ruby	Gorran Haven
p	FH716	Ruby Tuesday	St Mawes
p	E144	Ryds	Exmouth
p	DH42	Saint Petrox	Newlyn
p	Ex PZ677	Salamanda	Porthleven
p	BM502	Salamander	Newquay
p	SE74	Salcombe Lass	Salcombe
p	TH74	Saleda Blanche	Torquay
p	SS710	Sally	Hayle
p	PZ1191	Sally Rose of Navax	Hayle
	DH58	Saltpeter	Ex Dartmouth
p	E468	Salty I	Budleigh Salterton
p	E515	Sambe	Beer
p	FY817	Sammy Jayne	Mevagissey
p	PH350	Samphire	Plymouth
p	Ex SC8	Samson	Scilly
p	LI79	Sandella	Exmouth
p	Ex BM290	Sandra C	Appledore
p	PZ74	Sanluro	Newlyn
p	Ex TH115	Santoy	Ex Teignmouth
p	PZ66	Sapphire	Newlyn
p	PW23	Sarafine (Ex Laura B)	Scilly
p	BM30	Sara Lena	Brixham
p	PZ123	Sara Shaun	Newlyn
p	PZ545	Sarah Ann	Penzance
p	PZ753	Sarah C Stevenson	Newlyn
p	FH273	Sarah Jane of Helford	Hayle
p	PZ155	Sarah Jane-T	Newlyn
p	BM249	Sarah Jayne	Exmouth

p	PZ1218	Sarah Steve	Penzance
p	PZ22	Sarah-M	Newlyn
p	WY335	Sardia Louise	Newlyn
p	BM181	Sasha Emiel	Brixham
p	PH115	Sat Rat	River Tamar
p	FH85	Scath Du	Falmouth
p	PH356	Scathmas	Portwrinkle
p	PZ707	Scorpio	Cadgwith
p	BM102	Scorpion Lass	Brixham
p	SS32	Sea Breeze	Hayle
p	FH11	Sea Foam	Coverack
p	PZ62	Sea Fox	Newlyn
p	SM690	Sea Gem	Exmouth
p	PZ1199	Sea Goblin	Sennen Cove
p	Ex PZ110	Sea Hawk	Newlyn
p	PZ410	Sea Hunter	Newlyn
p	SS294	Sea Jay	St Ives
p	PZ882	Sea Lion	Newlyn
p	BM222	Sea Otter (ExBM19 & DS7)	Brixham
p	NT28	Sea Pie	Visitor
p	DH179	Sea Soldier	Dartmouth
p	PZ317	Sea Spirit	Newlyn
p	LT61	Sea Spray	Newlyn
	PW346	Sea Star	Ex Newlyn
p	FH611	Sea Urchin	Porthallow
p	SE2	Sea Vixen (Ex Salcombe)	Plymouth
p	PH619	Seagull	Porthallow
p	BM4	Seahunter	Brixham
p	BD247	Seaprose	Appledore
p	BD297	Selachos	Appledore
p	Ex NN88	Selina Ann	Ex Plymouth
p	E530	Selina Joy	Exmouth
p	PZ100	Semper Allegro	Newlyn
p	NN94	Semper Fidelis	Newlyn

ALPHABETICAL INDEX

p	Ex PH10	Sepia	Plymouth
p	BM165	Serena	Brixham
p	PZ642	Serene	Helford River
p	SS716	Shakari	St Ives
p	ExCA377	Shamrock	Seaton
p	E524	Shamrock	Seaton
p	TO46	Shamrock	Padstow
p	Ex SS40	Shamrock	Bude (Ex Newquay)
p	SH297	Shanice Patricia (Ex Nirvana)	Brixham
p	SS45	Shannon	Newquay
p	PW104	Sharicmar	Port Isaac
p	PZ807	Sharker	Mousehole
p	PZ590	She Wolf	Hayle
p	PH5576	Shell Belle	River Tamar
p	Ex FY315	Shelley Jane	Mevagissey
p	PH429	Shelley Marie	Plymouth
p	PZ77	Shelley Marie	Newlyn
p	Ex E47	Shemara	Seaton
p	Ex PH452	Sherlmar	Ex Plymouth (SANK)
p	PW186	Shiela Pat	Plymouth
p	BM35	Shiralee	Newlyn
p	PH585	Shiralee of Plymouth	River Tamar
p	Ex E133	Shirley Ann	Seaton (Ex Beer)
p	E99	Shona Elizabeth	Scilly
p	BM129	Shonalee	Paignton
p	PZ771	Silenus	Coverack
p	PZ1196	Silver Dawn	Falmouth
p	TH422	Silver Fox	Teignmouth
p	FH506	Silver Lance	St Ives
p	FH324	Silver Queen	Cadgwith
p	Ex PZ559	Silver Sides	Cape Cornwall
p	BM513	Silver Spray	Paignton

p	FR821	Silver Star	Visitor
p	PH411	Silver Stream	Plymouth
p	FY570	Silvery Sea	Porthleven
p	FY120	Sirene	Looe
p	DH63	Skerry Belle	Dartmouth
p	LA604	Skipper's Wife	Dartmouth
p	PH101	Snowdrop	Teignmouth
p	RX227	Soft Shadow	Mevagissey
p	FH443	Solitaire	Mevagissey
p	MN199	Solstice	Mevagissey
p	Ex E461	Someday Soon	Exmouth
p	FH494	Son-A-Mor	Coverack
p	LT22	Sophie Dawn	Brixham
p	E495	Sophie of Ladram	Exmouth
p	FY425	Southwind	Mevagissey
p	PZ5	Sou'wester	Penzance
p	FH25	Sovereign	Newlyn
p	PZ14	Sowenna	Newlyn
p	PZ15	Spaven Mor (Ex P'Leven)	Plymouth
p	Ex F11	Speedwell	Padstow
p	PZ86	Spilgarn	Portreath
p	PH307	Splendour	Plymouth
p	PZ218	Sprigs of Heather	Newlyn
	FH168	Spring Tide	Helford River
p	Ex PH90	Squilla	Ex Plymouth
p	Ex LT266	Srenex Fidelis	Ex Brixham
p	PZ64	St Elvan	Porthleven
p	PZ1053	St Georges	Newlyn
p	E484	St Nicholas II	Teignmouth
p	FH243	St Ruan	Porthleven
p	PZ68	Starfish	Porthleven
p	FH414	Starlight	Cadgwith
p	Ex E183	Stella Maris	Exmouth

ALPHABETICAL INDEX

p	WK349	Stephanie	Bideford
p	FH728	Sterennyk	Helford River
p	PZ428	Stergan	Hayle
p	B522	Still Waters	Plymouth
p	Ex SS209	Still Waters	St Ives
p	FY3	Storm Child	Plymouth
p	Ex ML313	Storm Child (Now BM2)	Ex Polperro
p	E9	Stormy Dawn	Sidmouth
	Ex FH345	Stormy Petrel	Ex Helford River
p	PW443	Strike	Exmouth
p	E163	Striker	Exmouth
p	E505	Stroma	Budleigh Salterton
p	PH24	Su Jean	Padstow
p	FH1	Sula	Coverack
p	PH25	Sula Bassana	River Tamar
	E16	Sula Bassana	Ex Exmouth
p	Ex FY840	Sumita	Polperro
p	Ex SE1	Summerwine	Teignmouth
p	E94	Sunbeam	Seaton
p	FH222	Sundowner	Newquay
p	FR359	Sunrise	Visitor
p	SE29	Sunseeker II	Brixham
p	FY826	Sunshine	Mevagissey
p	E284	Sunshine	Sidmouth
p	M65	Sunstar	Scilly
p	FY509	Superb II	Mevagissey
p	DH99	Superb-Us	Brixham
p	PH583	Surf Hunter	Newquay
p	FY759	Surprise	Mevagissey
p	FY101	Susan 1	Looe
p	Ex FY575	Susie	Ex Looe
p	HL1054	Suvera	Brixham
	PZ454	Suzie	Ex St Ives
p	FY59	Swallow	Looe

p	SC46	Swan Dancer	Scilly
p	Ex PH79	Sweet Home	Plymouth
p	FH697	Sweet Promise	Falmouth
p	H145	Swift	Hayle
p	SE11	Swift	Salcombe
p	Ex PH473	Swift	Dartmouth
p	FY825	Swiftsure	Ex Looe
p	BM12	Sydo	Brixham
p	WH454	T K	Bude
p	PZ280	Talisman	Helford River
p	FH484	Tallula (Ex Tela)	Looe (Ex Falmouth)
p	PW107	Tallula	Newquay
p	FH340	Tamalin	Porthoustock
	FH232	Tamara	Ex Padstow
p	FY332	Tamara	Mevagissey
p	PZ564	Tamara	Sennen Cove
p	PH34	Tamesis II	Plymouth
p	PZ315	Tamsin T	Newlyn
p	FY778	Taregan (Ex Sirene))	Looe
p	PZ611	Tan-Nos	Newlyn
p	PZ209	Tara	Lamorna Cove
	SE71	Tardy	Salcombe
p	Ex SE26	Tarka	Salcombe
p	PZ17	Teal	Lamorna Cove
p	SS88	Tegen Mor	Hayle
p	FY863	Temeraire	Looe
p	DH95	Tenacious	Salcombe
p	BM46	TT BM249 Sarah Jayne	Brixham
p	Ex SE21	Tender to SW Lady	Salcombe
p	BM488	Thankful	Brixham
p	PZ8	The Boss	Newlyn
p	PW214	Thomas Andrew	Padstow
p	BM522	Thon B	Brixham
p	FH339	Three Boys	Mevagissey

p	KY467	Three Boys	Exmouth
p	PZ718	Three Boys (Now Eel-Avum)	Penzance
p	TH119	Three Fevers	Teignmouth
p	FY1	Three Jays	Gorran Haven
p	E507	Three Jays	Bude
p	PW371	Three J's	Newquay
p	BM273	Three Sisters	Brixham
p	BM169	Three Sons (Ex Marilyn Jane)	Brixham
p	Ex PH463	Tiburon	Plymouth
p	Ex PH579	Tiddler	Ex Plymouth
p	SS76	Tillerman	St Ives
p	BS186	Tjeerd Jackoba	Plymouth
p	TN2	Tobrach-N	Visitor
p	SS40	Tollbar	Newquay
p	M11	Torri Gwnt	St Ives
p	DR120	Touch of Madness	Barnstaple
p	SS67	Tracey Clare	Helford River
p	E451	Treble TTT	Exmouth
p	PZ23	Treen	Newlyn
p	PZ49	Treglown (Ex La Mouette)	Hayle
p	FH395	Treneglos	Falmouth
p	PZ193	Trevessa IV	Newlyn
p	PW64	Trevose of Newquay	Newlyn
p	FY776	Trewartha	Mevagissey
p	PZ196	Trewarvaneth	Newlyn
p	PZ2	Trident II	Mousehole
p	PH117	Trio	Plymouth
p	BM219	Triton	Brixham
p	TH148	Triton (Ex Plymouth)	Newlyn
p	DH387	True Grit	Brixham
p	FY806	Trya	Looe
p	SS233	Tryphena	Newquay
	PZ499	Twilight	Ex Newlyn
p	PZ137	Twilight III	Newlyn

p	PZ1212	Two Boys	Newlyn
p	SE3	Two Boys	Salcombe
p	BM516	Two Brothers	Brixham
p	SM241	Two Brothers	Exmouth
p	FY850	Typhoon	Looe
p	PZ888	Utsker	Newlyn
p	Ex FH270	Valerie May/waits PZReg	Newlyn (Ex Looe)
p	BH9	Valhalla	Brixham
p	FY813	Valiant	Falmouth
p	TH417	Valkyrie	Teignmouth
p	BM362	Van Dijck	Brixham
p	PZ166	Venture	Newlyn
p	FY58	Venus	Mevagissey
p	Ex PZ111	Veracity	Dartmouth
p	Ex PH487	Verity	Salcombe
p	DS11	Vertrouwen	Visitor
p	FY30	Vesper II	Mevagissey
p	FY529	Vesta	Fowey
p	SC32	Vicky Anna	Scilly
p	CK923	Victoria	Looe
p	FH706	Victoria Ann	Cadgwith
p	SC11	Victory of Helford	Scilly
p	PZ88	Viking (Charters)	Penzance
p	Ex FY854	Viking Girl	Ex Polperro
p	PZ481	Vipa	St Ives
p	OB254	Virgo	Brixham
p	E455	Volunteer	Exmouth
p	WY1	Walrus	Ilfracombe
p	PH60	Warrior	Plymouth
p	FY803	Wave II	Mevagissey
p	SS252	Wayfarer	Newlyn
p	Ex SH76	Wayfinder	Newlyn
	PZ3	We-re Here	Ex Penzance
	SE371	West Wind	Ex Dartmouth

p	Ex PH224	Western Enterprise	Plymouth
p	Ex FH185	Whistle	Falmouth
p	Ex FH34	White Heather	Fowey
p	PZ272	White Heather	St Ives
p	PZ25	White Rose	Porthgwarra
	ExFH321	William and Molly	Ex Scilly
p	PZ75	William Harvey	Newlyn
p	DH5	William Henry II	Dartmouth
p	PZ191	William S Stevenson	Newlyn
p	PZ195	William Stevenson	Newlyn
p	FH646	Willow	Falmouth
p	PW393	Winnie the Pooh	Port Isaac
p	NN734	Winter's Tale	Appledore
p	PH110	Wiron 1	Plymouth
p	PH220	Wiron 2	Plymouth
p	Ex E500	Woody	Budleigh Salter ton
	DH145	Xavier	Dartmouth
p	FY276	Zadok	Plymouth
p	WH707	Zaranathax	Plymouth
p	PW122	Zarvan	Newquay
p	FH712	Zephron	Portloe
p	DH180	Ziggy	Torcross
p	E23	Zoe of Ladram	Exmouth
p	TO4	Zona	Falmouth
p	DH15	Zoom	Dartmouth

ALPHANUMERICAL INDEX by REGISTRATION NUMBER

	Devon & Cornwall		Registered Fishing Vessels		
p' indicates photo taken					
	A	**Aberdeen**			
	AB	**Aberystwyth**			
p	AB199	Pathfinder	Out of Area	8.5m	Newquay
	AD	**Ardrossan**			
	AH	**Arbroath**			
p	AH32	Ajax	Netter	17m	Newlyn
p	AH101	Girl Soo	Netter	8m	Plymouth
	BF	**Banff**			
	AR	**Ayr**			
	B	**Belfast**			
p	B80	Green Isles II	Whelker	11.5m	Ilfracombe
p	B522	Still Waters	Trawler	9.87m	Newlyn
p	B953	J-Lee	Trawler	9.93m	Newlyn
	BA	**Ballantrae**			
p	BA45	Charisma	Netter	16.4m	Padstow
p	BA87	King Challenger	Scalloper	21.3m	Visitor
p	Ex BA816	Jaycee	De-registered	9.99m	Ex Looe
	BCK	**Buckie**			
p	BCK81	Kestrel	Scalloper	30.21m	Visitor
p	BCK160	Blue Angel	Beam Trawler	33.4m	Brixham
p	BCK222	Emily Jane	Scalloper	36m	Visitor
	BD	**Bideford**			
p	BD1	Cerulean	Trawler	14.98m	Appledore
	BD2	Lundy Star		8m	Bideford
p	BD9	Anna	Netter	7.5m	Appledore
p	Ex BD10	Estrel Do Mar	De-registered	8.0m	Appledore
p	BD18	Gemini	Netter	7.1m	Porthleven
	BD33	Hannah Marie		9.94m	Bideford
p	BD69	Neptune	Angler	6.4m	Clovelly
p	BD76	Boy Lee	Trawler	9.8m	Bideford
	BD97	Ocean Monarch		8.1m	Ex Bude
p	BD109	Georgina	De-registered	8.84m	Ilfracombe
p	Ex BD125	Un named	De-registered	<5m	River Tamar
	BD128	Gladys Jean		4.0m	Ex Bideford
	BD155	Toby II		4.82m	Ex Ilfracombe
	BD169	Jo		3.69m	Ex Ilfracombe
p	BD220	Lundy Star	Potter/Angler	8.0m	Bideford
p	BD247	Seaprose	Trawler	9.9m	Appledore
	BD249	Pair I		5.35m	Ex Bideford
p	BD257	Mallagar	Trawler	9.8m	Brixham
p	BD277	Our Olivia Belle	Trawler	14.95m	Bideford
p	BD279	Ceri-Lee	Potter	4.5m	Clovelly
p	Ex BD282	Argo	De-registered	<10m	Appledore
p	Ex BD283	Melanie Anne	De-registered	5m	Bude
p	BD287	Our Josie Grace	Trawler	14.95m	Ilfracombe
p	BD290	Mermaid	Potter	4.88m	Clovelly
p	Ex BD291		De-registered	<10m	Appledore
p	BD292	Bombay	Potter	4.5m	Clovelly
p	BD296	Marlin	Out of Area	7.3m	Ex Ilfracombe
p	BD297	Selachos	Angler	5.95m	Appledore
	BE	**Barnstaple**			
	BE3	Dolphin		6.0m	Barnstaple
p	BE6	Otter	Netter	4.4m	Barnstaple
	Ex BE7	Mar	De-registered	4.88m	Barnstaple
p	BE9	October Morning	Net/Pot/Angl	8.07m	Lynmouth
	BE13	Carla Jane		4.54m	Bideford
	Ex BE27	Morning Star	De-registered	4.65m	Barnstaple
p	BE29	K-Sands	Netter	3.8m	Appledore
	BE31	Tanya		5.07m	Barnstaple
p	Ex BE83	Kingfisher	De-registered	6.93m	Ex Lynmouth
p	BE83	Kingfisher	Potter	6.99m	Lynmouth
p	BE85	Jack	Netter	4.05m	Appledore
	BF	**Banff**			
	BH	**Blyth**			
p	BH9	Valhalla	Trawler	18.15m	Brixham
	BK	**Berwick**			

p	BK524	Kindly Light D	Netter	7.45m	Helford R.iver
	BL	**Bristol**			
p	BL31	Mischief	Potter	4.8m	Dartmouth
	BM	**Brixham**			
p	BM1	Guyona	Trawler	13.1m	Brixham
p	BM2	Hannah D	Netter	10.0m	Brixham
p	BM4	Seahunter	Trawler	12.2m	Brixham
p	BM5	Dee-J	Trawler	10m	Brixham
p	BM6	Reel One	Tender		Brixham
p	BM7	Lady Maureen	Beam Trawler	34.15m	Brixham
	BM10	Emelia M Ethel	Beam Trawler	23m	Brixham
p	BM11	Liam John II	Netter	5.7m	Torquay
p	BM12	Sydo	Trawler	13.8m	Brixham
p	Ex BM19	Sea Otter	Now BM222	15.2m	Brixham
p	BM23	Carhelmar	Beam Trawler	23.8m	Brixham
p	BM24	Peace & Plenty III	Trawler	11.7m	Brixham
p	BM27	Our Miranda	Beam Trawler	25.28m	Brixham
p	BM28	Angel Emiel	Beam Trawler	23.1m	Brixham
p	Ex BM38	Provident	Trawler (sail)		Brixham
p	BM30	Sara Lena	Beam Trawler	18.2m	Brixham
p	BM35	Shiralee	Trawler	9.8m	Newlyn
p	BM40	Boy Philip	Potter	5.6m	Torquay
p	BM44	Nipper	Potter	5.9m	Brixham
p	BM46	TT SarahJayne	Tender	5.9m	Brixham
p	BM51	Harm Johannes	Beam Trawler	25.4	Brixham
p	BM55	Kryst-Le-Kay	Netter	9.3m	Brixham
p	BM66	Mar Rose	Potter	8.0m	Brixham
p	BM67	Gina Louise	Trawler	12.5m	Brixham
	BM75	Carefree		7.4m	Ex Brixham
p	BM76	Hell-of-a-Dear	Out of Area	6.6m	ExTeignmouth
p	Ex BM76	Vigilance	Trawler (Sail)	22m	Brixham
p	BM77	Jacoba	Beam Trawler	27m	Brixham
p	BM79	Adela	Trawler	9.2m	Brixham
p	BM87	Les Mercenaires	Sank Nov 05	10.0m	Ex Brixham
p	Ex BM98	Little Boy Blue	De-registered	4.3m	Paignton
p	BM98	Little Boy Blue	Potter	4.85m	Paignton

p	BM100	Cheryl of Ladram	Beam Trawler	30.3m	Plymouth
p	BM102	Scorpion Lass	Netter/Liner	6.1m	Brixham
	BM107	Sister MCB		6.7m	Ex Brixham
p	BM115	My Mikaela	Trawler	9.98m	Brixham
p	BM127	Harvester x E496	Trawl /Scallop	14.15m	Brixham
p	BM128	Lady Lou	Beam Trawler	28.2m	Brixham
p	BM129	Shonalee	Potter	5.6m	Paignton
p	BM140	Geeske	Scalloper	30.4m	Brixham
p	BM147	Malkerry	Trawler	13.7m	Brixham
p	BM150	Our Maria	Netter	10m	Brixham
	Ex BM158	Michelle Louisa	De-registered	22.5m	Ex Brixham
	Ex BM165	Sarah Louise	Now BM510	24m	Brixham
p	BM165	Serena	Trawl/Scallop	9.98m	Brixham
p	BM166	Lerina	Trawler		Brixham
p	BM169	Three Sons Ex Marilyn Jayne	Beam Trawler	26.2m	Brixham
p	BM172	Our Johanna	Beam Trawler	26.2m	Brixham
p	BM176	Ebonnie	Crabber	14.95m	Brixham
p	BM177	La Creole	Potter	12.7m	Brixham
p	BM181	Sasha Emiel	Beam Trawler	33.9m	Brixham
p	BM188	Lloyd Tyler	Beam Trawler	26.2m	Brixham
p	BM190	Marina	Trawler	13.0m	Brixham
p	BM192	Rachel Louis	Trawler		Brixham
p	Ex BM202	OnzeLinquenda	Scrapped 04	26.4m	Ex Brixham
p	BM208	Jacomina	Beam Trawler	25.2m	Brixham
p	BM218	Haringvliet	Beam Trawler	29.8m	Brixham
p	BM219	Triton	Angler	6.3m	Brixham
p	Ex BM222	Mourne Lass	De-registered	15.8m	Brixham
p	BM222	Sea Otter ExDS7	Trawl/Scallop	15.24m	Brixham
p	BM234	De Vrouw Marie	Beam Trawler	30.4m	Brixham
	BM237	Jessica Louise	Potter	9.95m	Mull
p	BM241	Magdalena	Beam Trawler	29.9m	Brixham
p	BM247	Arcomine	De-registered	30.7m	Ex Brixham
p	BM248	Jacky J	Potter	8.3m	Brixham
p	BM249	Sarah Jayne	Trawl/Scallop	14.9m	Exmouth

ALPHANUMERICAL INDEX by REGISTRATION NUMBER

	BM254	Blue Gate	Trawler/Netter	38.59m	Spain
	BM257	Eder Sands	Liner	38.2m	Spain
p	BM258	Helen Claire	Potter	14.4m	Brixham
p	BM264	Our Zoe Anne	Beam Trawler /Scalloper	29.9m	Brixham
p	BM265	Joanna C	Scalloper	14.8m	Brixham
p	BM273	Three Sisters	Netter/Potter	7.1m	Teignmouth
p	BM278	Ondarruman	Trawler	33.8m	Visitor
p	BM282	Catear	Trawler	29m	Brixham
p	Ex BM290	Sandra C	De-registered	5.7m	Appledore
	Ex BM294	Bootneck	De-registered	7.31m	
	BM297	Mountain Peak	Trawler	39.9m	Spain
p	BM298	George Johannes	Beam Trawler	26.2m	Newlyn
p	BM342	Our Wendy	Potter/Liner	5.0m	Torquay
p	BM361	Barentszee	Beam Trawler	30.6m	Plymouth
p	BM362	Van Dijck	Scalloper	33.5m	Brixham
p	BM367	Bon Accord	Trawler	14.93m	Looe
	BM372	Ability		5.8m	Anglesey
	Ex BM378	Sumita	De-registered	7.5m	
	Ex BM444	Our Venture	Now K355	11.2m	Ex Brixham
p	Ex BM474	Mystere	De-registered	5.5m	Brixham
p	BM476	Lady Maggie	Netter/Potter	5.9m	Salcombe
	BM477	Boy Paul		9.7m	Peterhead
p	BM478	Danielle	Scalloper	31.99m	Brixham
p	BM479	Lisa K	Trawler	9.8m	Brixham
	BM481	Loyal Friend		10.0m	Buckie
p	BM482	Mary Anne	Trawler	11.98m	Brixham
p	BM484	Constant Friend	Trawl/Scalloper	14.95m	Brixham
p	Ex BM485	Christinie	De-registered	9.9m	Ex Brixham
p	BM487	Hartley	Trawler	11.7m	Looe
p	BM488	Thankful	Potter	7.6m	Brixham
p	Ex BM489	Nirvana	Now SH297	9.96m	Brixham
	BM490	Frank Phillips	Out of Area	9.85m	Ex Brixham
p	BM491	Nicola Jayne	Angler	5.0m	Brixham
p	BM492	Maggie	Potter	5.6m	River Yealm

	Ex BM493	Ocean Spirit	Now PD493	13.7m	Peterhead
	Ex BM496	Endurance	De-registered	10m	Ex Brixham
p	BM498	Emerald	Trawler	9.95m	Torquay
p	BM499	Atlantis II	Potter	10.0m	Teignmouth
p	BM502	Salamander	Potter	9.5m	Newquay
p	BM503	J C K	Potter	5.7m	Brixham
p	BM508	Jose Jacqueline	Fish Farm	11.5m	Brixham
p	BM510	Angus Rose	Beam Trawler	24.0m	Brixham
p	BM511	Magnum	Netter	5.6m	Newlyn
p	BM513	Silver Spray	Potter	5.63m	Paignton
p	BM516	Two Brothers	Trawler	9.99m	Brixham
p	BM517	Kasey Marie	Scalloper	13.4m	Brixham
p	BM522	Thon-B	Fish Farm		Brixham
p	BM2000	Lady T Emiel	Beam Trawler	32.8m	Brixham
	BN	**Boston**			
	BO	**Borrowstoness**			
	BR	**Bridgwater**			
	BRD	**Broadford**			
p	BRD92	J-Anne	Trawler	8.9m	Newlyn
p	ExBRD222	Carrie Jane	De-registered	9.7m	Looe
	BS	**Beaumaris**			
p	BS186	Tjeerd Jackoba	Scalloper	26.3m	Visitor
p	BS472	Elise (Ex Gwenfaen)	Trawler	9.9m	Brixham
	BU	**Burntisland**			
	BW	**Barrow**			
p	Ex BW40	Hazy Dawn	De-registered	6.2m	Ex Brixham
	CA	**Cardigan**			
p	Ex CA44	Innisfree	De-registered	6.4m	Ex Paignton
p	Ex CA377	Shamrock	De-registered		Seaton
	CE	**Coleraine**	**(Ireland)**		
	CF	**Cardiff**			
p	CF1	Nemesis	Scalloper	9.9m	Plymouth
	CH	**Chester**			
	CK	**Colchester**			
p	Ex CK181	Mini-Me	De-registered	4.94m	Looe

ALPHANUMERICAL INDEX by REGISTRATION NUMBER

p	CK923	Victoria	Netter/Liner	9.9m	Looe
	CL	**Carlisle**			
p	CL22	Don Valley	Trawler	9.8m	Plymouth
	CN	**Campbeltown**			
p	CN119	Islander	Potter	6.2m	Mousehole
p	CN187	Nova Spero	Netter/Trawler	20.4m	Newlyn
	CO	**Caernarvon**			
p	CO365	Celtic Pride	Trawl /Scallop	12m	Looe
	CS	**Cowes**			
p	Ex CS112	Northern Kiwi	De-registered	<6m	Porthoustock
p	CS295	Katy	Liner	4.4m	Gorran Haven
	CT	**Castletown**	**(I.O.M.)**		
	CY	**Castlebay**	**(Barra)**		
	DE	**Dundee**			
	DH	**Dartmouth**			
p	DH1	Nicky V	Potter	9.8m	Dartmouth
p	DH5	William Henry II	Netter/Potter	22.5m	Dartmouth
p	DH8	Mayfly	Netter	7.27m	Dartmouth
p	Ex DH10		De-registered		Ex Brixham
p	DH11	Miranda	Potter	4.8m	Beesands
p	DH15	Zoom	Angler	5.7m	Dartmouth
p	DH17	Excel	Potter	15.2m	Dartmouth
p	DH20	Magnum	Netter/Potter	11.3m	Dartmouth
p	DH21	Rob Roy	Potter	4.3m	Beesands
	DH24	Westerly Warrior	Netter	9.99m	Ross
	DH26	Felicity		4.4m	Dartmouth
p	DH42	Saint Petrox	Netter	7.8m	Newlyn
p	DH46	Independent	Potter	10.6m	Brixham
	DH50	Shirley Betty	Potter	9.81m	Poole
	DH58	Saltpeter		3.1m	Dartmouth
p	DH60	Maggie Marie	Trawler	9.3m	Dartmouth
p	DH62	Moonfleet	Potter	5.6m	Beesands
p	DH63	Skerry Belle	Potter	11.5m	Dartmouth
	DH71	Crusader of Kingswear	Potter	16.9m	Dartmouth

p	DH74	Pisces	Angler	4.9m	Beesands
p	DH76	Heatseeker	Potter	9.9m	Dartmouth
p	DH77	Dawn	Netter	4.3m	Torcross
	DH79	Tender		3.5m	Dartmouth
p	DH82	Lucky Dip	Angler	4.5m	Salcombe
p	DH86	Dawn Raider	Angler	4.5m	Torcross
p	DH88	Rejoice	Potter	6.2m	Dartmouth
p	DH89	Bobolink	Angler	4.7m	Dartmouth
p	DH92	P.W.S.	Netter	4.4m	Torcross
p	DH95	Tenacious	Trawler/Potter	15.1m	Salcombe
p	DH97	Full Monty	Angler	7.8m	Dartmouth
p	DH99	Superb-Us	Trawler	13.6m	Brixham
	DH100	Edward Henry	Potter	25.5m	Scrabster
	DH104	Purbeck Isle	Potter	11.64m	Weymouth
	DH110	Kingfisher	Potter	18.4m	Scrabster
p	DH119	Northern Clipper	Potter	13m	Dartmouth
p	DH133	Damsel Fly	Potter	9.3m	Dartmouth
p	DH135	Our Pammy	Potter	8.5m	Dartmouth
p	DH141	Britannia of Beesands	Crabber	9.99m	Dartmouth
	Ex DH144	Moonfire of Galmpton	De-registered	9.2m	Ex Brixham
	DH145	Xavier		4.8m	Ex Dartmouth
	DH148	Royal Sovereign	Potter	16.06m	Ireland
p	DH149	Newbrook	Potter	14.3m	Dartmouth
p	DH179	Sea Soldier	Potter	5.9m	Dartmouth
	DH176	Bon Amy	Potter	9.6m	Scrabster
p	DH180	Ziggy	Netter/Angler	3.9m	Torcross
p	DH183	Joint Venture	Potter	8.0m	Dartmouth
p	DH300	Jodie Ann	Netter/Potter	6.7m	Teignmouth
p	DH384	DVFG	Angler	5.7m	Dartmouth
p	DH387	True Grit	Netter/Potter	9.2m	Brixham
p	DH388	Cassius J	Netter/Potter	6.8m	Padstow
p	DH390	Nil Desperandum	Potter	9.0m	Dartmouth
p	DH392	Elm	Netter	3.7m	Dartmouth
p	DH394	Dianne T	Potter	4.0m	Dartmouth
p	DH397	Ebony Rose	Angler	4.27m	Dartmouth

ALPHANUMERICAL INDEX by REGISTRATION NUMBER

p	DH399	Ahab	Netter	4.69m	Torcross
p	DH405	Deejay	Netter	4.7m	Dartmouth
	DO	**Douglas (I.O.M.)**			
	DR	**Dover**			
p	DR120	Touch of Madness	Netter	6.43m	Barnstaple
p	DR166	Gipsy King	Netter	7.4m	Padstow
	DS	**Dumfries**			
p	DS10	Albion	Scalloper	34.9m	Visitor
p	DS11	Vertrouwen	Scalloper	26.24m	Visitor
	E	**Exeter**			
p	E4	Garn	Netter/Potter	4.8m	Budleigh S'ton
p	E6	Evelyn	Out of Area	7.9m	Ex Brixham
p	E9	Stormy Dawn	Potter	6.01m	Sidmouth
p	E14	Heart of Oak	Potter	9.99m	Plymouth
p	E15	Kimberley	Not registered	<5m	Exmouth
	E16	Sula Bassana	Out of Area	10.0m	Ex Exmouth
p	Ex E18	Barbara Mae	De-registered	7.1m	Seaton
p	E19	(Unnamed)	Not registered	<5m	Exmouth
p	E20	Karli-N	Netter	8.0m	River Tamar
p	E22	Roanne	Potter	4.1m	Exmouth
p	E23	Zoe of Ladram	Netter/Potter	8.85m	Exmouth
p	E25	Otter	Netter	3.8m	Budleigh S'ton
p	E28	My Lady	Potter	5.6m	Seaton
p	E30	Cygnet	Out of Area	8.0m	Ex Beer
	E32	Two Brothers		6.0m	Ex Exmouth
p	E43	Lily May	Potter/Angler	5.8m	Beer
p	E44	Arandora Star	Netter/Potter	8.5m	River Tamar
p	Ex E47	Shemara	De-registered	6.9m	Seaton
p	Ex E53	Elsie	De-registered		Exmouth
	E58	Miss Pattie	Trawler/Netter	9.9m	Lyme Regis
	E68	Sea Seeker	Trawler	11.2m	Lyme Regis
	E73	Becci	Out of Area	5.0m	Ex Exmouth
p	E74	Louise	Angler	5.7m	Exmouth
p	E87	Provider	Trawler	9.95m	Exmouth
p	E88	Margaret of Ladram	Beam Trawler	32m	Plymouth

p	E92	Esme	Salmon Netter	4.3m	Exmouth
p	E94	Sunbeam	Potter	6.5m	Seaton
p	E99	Shona Elizabeth	Netter/Liner	8.44m	Scilly
p	Ex E117	Lively Lady	De-registered	7.3m	Beer
p	E123	Emily J	Trawler	11.95m	Exmouth
p	E127	Barbara Jean	Potter/Angler	7.1m	Beer
p	Ex E133	Shirley Ann	De-registered	6.4m	Seaton
p	E144	Ryds	Netter	4.7m	Exmouth
p	E146	Dorado	Netter	7.6m	West Bay
	E147	Sir Ivor		6.1m	Portland
p	E161	Our Endeavour	Trawler	10m	Plymouth
p	E163	Striker	Tender	5.1m	Exmouth
p	E167	Frances Jane	Angler	7.3m	Lyme Regis
p	Ex E183	Stella Maris	De-registered	11.7m	Exmouth
p	E201	Antelma	Potter	6.5m	Lyme Regis
p	E217	Marta	Netter	4.0m	Sidmouth
p	E225	Joy of Ladram	Beam Trawler	37.75m	Plymouth
	E227	Julie	Out of Area	4.1m	Ex Exmouth
p	E249	Blue Lady	Potter	6.8m	Beer
p	E256	Martha-D	Potter	7.0m	Seaton
	E262	Lucky Seven	Potter	10.29m	Lulworth
p	Ex E271	Bee J	De-registered	7.8m	Ex Beer
p	Ex E274	Dickie Bird II	De-registered	6.2m	Seaton
	Ex E276	Pirate II	De-registered	3.8m	Ex Exmouth
p	E282	Adbrenat	Potter	7.3m	Beer
p	E284	Sunshine	Potter	5.6m	Sidmouth
P	Ex E289	Pearl II	De-registered	6.8m	Beer
p	E444	Girl Debra	Trawl/Scalloper	15.0m	Brixham
	Ex E445	Barney	De-registered	4.4m	Ex Exmouth
p	E449	Lucy M	Angler	5.1m	Exmouth
p	E451	Treble TTT	Potter	7.1m	Exmouth
p	E455	Volunteer	Netter	4.8m	Exeter
p	E456	Little Gem	Tender	5.0m	Brixham
p	E457	Francis B	Netter	5.0m	Sidmouth
p	E458	Emily B	Potter	6.4m	Portreath

p	E460	Gus	Potter	5.15m	Sidmouth
p	Ex E461	Someday Soon	De-registered	5.3m	Exmouth
p	E468	Salty I	Netter/Potter	4.4m	Budleigh S'ton
	E472	CJ 1	Out of Area	5.1m	Ex Exmouth
p	Ex E476	Margh An Mor	De-registered	6.0m	Exmouth
p	E484	St Nicholas II	Trawler	6.1m	Teignmouth
p	E487	Betty's Boys	Trawler/ Potter	6.52m	Seaton
	E488	Golden Fleece	Potter	9.95m	Antrim
	Ex E492	Spider II	De-registered	4.6m	Ex Exmouth
p	E495	Amy-R (Ex Sophie of Ladram)	Trawler/Scalloper	14.97m	Brixham
p	Ex E496	Joy of Ladram	(Now BM127)	14.15m	Brixham
p	Ex E500	Woody	De-registered	4.2m	Budleigh S'ton
p	E505	Stroma	Netter/Potter	3.97m	Budleigh S'ton
p	E507	Three Jays	Out of Area	7.6m	Ex Bude
p	E508	Becci of Ladram	Netter/Potter	9.8m	Exmouth
p	E513	Outcast	Potter	4.5m	Seaton
p	E515	Sambe	Potter	8.0m	Beer
p	E516	Alibi	Mussel Dredger	9.95m	Exmouth
p	E519	Rene	Potter	6m	Sidmouth
p	E520	Mia B	Potter	9.95m	Exmouth
p	E521	Rowella of Ladram	Whelker	11.9m	Exmouth
p	E523	Good Life	Liner/Netter	5.5m	Seaton
p	E524	Shamrock	Liner	5.8m	Seaton
p	E527	Annie	Potter	5.5m	Beer
p	E530	Selina Joy	Potter	10.0m	Exmouth
p	E533	Prosperity	Netter	8.35m	Exmouth
p	E534	Attitude	Netter/Potter	9.02m	Exmouth
p	E535	Betty-G(ExNN716)	Scalloper	9.9m	Exmouth
	F	**Faversham**			
p	Ex F11	Speedwell	To be Re-registered		Padstow
	FD	**Fleetwood**			
p	FD100	Christina	Beam Trawler	28m	Brixham

p	Ex FD114	Ora et Labora	De-Regis tered	30.5m	Brixham
	Ex FD508	Kon Tiki	De-registerec		Ex Newlyn
	FE	**Folkestone**			
	FH	**Falmouth**			
p	FH1	Sula	Liner	6.1m	Coverack
p	FH2	Olga Annie	Netter	6.0m	Falmouth
p	FH5	Regina Maris	Netter/Liner	12.38m	Ex Helford R.
p	FH11	Sea Foam	Netter	7.4m	Coverack
p	FH12	Morel Margh	Scalloper	10.9m	Falmouth
p	FH21	Misty Blue	Angler	5.8m	Falmouth
p	FH23	Iona	Netter	4.5m	Portscatho
p	FH25	Sovereign	Netter/Potter	8.0m	Newlyn
p	Ex FH34	White Heather	Sail Yawl		Fowey
	Ex FH49	Marigold	De-registered	4.1m	Ex Cadgwith
p	FH55	Patrice II	Netter/Liner	7.8m	Falmouth
p	FH57	Foxy lady	Liner	4.74m	Porthoustock
p	FH58	Billeric	Potter	5.6m	Falmouth.
	FH71	Southern Star		7.3m	Ex Coverack
p	FH75	Jasmine	Potter	5.3m	Portloe
p	FH76	Galwad-Y-Mor	Trawler	11.9m	Mevagissey
p	FH85	Scath Du	Potter	5.8m	Falmouth
p	FH88	Karenza Jayne	Netter	6.62m	Helford R.
p	FH89	Cariad	Netter/Liner	7.3m	Falmouth
p	FH93	Ida May	Potter	4.5m	Church Cove
	Ex FH95	Karlyn	De-registered	5.6m	Ex Coverack
	Ex FH96	Heart of Oak	De-registered	13.4m	Ex Helford R.
p	FH106	Flying Breeze	Netter/Liner	6.2m	Coverack
p	FH109	Maria Q	Netter/Potter	8.1m	Mevagissey
p	FH121	Britannia V	Netter	15.5m	Newlyn
p	FH130	Gemma Claire	Potter/Liner	<5m	Scilly
	Ex FH145	Broadsword/Mylor	De-registered	8.6m	Maldon
p	Ex FH151	Liberator	De-registered		Ex Portholland
	FH168	Spring Tide		5.7m	Helford R.
p	Ex FH176	Milly	De-registered	5.8m	Coverack

ALPHANUMERICAL INDEX by REGISTRATION NUMBER

p	Ex FH185	Whistle	De-registered		Falmouth
p	FH187	Kon-Tiki	Netter	4.3m	Helford R.
	Ex FH189	Er-an-Mor	De-registered	5.7m	Ex Cadgwith
	Ex FH191	Andramaque	De-registered	11.9m	Ex Falmouth
p	FH198	Harvester	Potter	11.0m	Ex Falmouth
p	FH200	Jen Lou II	Netter/Liner	5.0m	Porthoustock
p	FH206	Golden Fleece	Trawl/Scalloper	13.9m	Falmouth
p	Ex FH209	Blue Minstrel	De-registered	8.1m	Falmouth
p	FH214	Lady Hamilton	Netter/Liner	8.5m	Helford R.
p	FH222	Sundowner	Netter/Potter	9.3m	Newquay
p	Ex FH229	Newlek-Mor	De-registered	4.9m	Portreath
	FH232	Tamara	Out of Area	8.2m	Whitby
p	FH243	St Ruan	Netter	9.9m	Porthleven
p	FH246	Gamgy Lady	Potter	9.2m	Falmouth
p	FH253	Petite Angela	Trawler	10m	Brixham
p	FH258	Kendore	Trawler	9.9m	Brixham
p	Ex FH270	Valerie May	Trawler	10.4m	Newlyn
p	FH273	Sarah Jane/Helford	Netter/Potter	7.5m	Hayle
p	FH280	Evening Star	Netter/Potter	6.3m	Coverack
p	FH289	Elizabeth Madeline	Potter	8.6m	Newquay
p	FH293	Girl Pauline	Netter/Liner	5.3m	Porthoustock
p	FH300	Paula Rose	Potter	7.2m	Falmouth
p	FH322	Bobbie Dee II	Scallop/Netter	10.8m	River Fal
p	FH324	Silver Queen	Potter	7.2m	Cadgwith
p	FH339	Three Boys	Net/Pot/Liner	5.5m	Mevagissey
p	FH340	Tamalin	Liner	5.0m	Porthoustock
	Ex FH345	Stormy Petrel	De-registered	5.8m	Ex Helford R.
p	FH353	Jane Louise	Potter	7.75m	Falmouth
p	FH395	Treneglos	Netter	8.1m	Falmouth
	FH398	Isabelle	Out of Area	6.4m	Bridlington
p	FH414	Starlight	Netter/Potter	7.6m	Cadgwith
p	FH416	Emma May	Netter	7.3m	Looe
p	FH442	Properjob	Dive Boat	4.7m	Falmouth
p	FH443	Solitaire	Netter/Liner	6.5m	Mevagissey
p	FH468	Girl Jan	Net/Pot/Line	6.3m	Porthoustock
p	FH484	Tallula (Ex Tela)	Netter	7.6m	Looe

p	FH485	Leviathan	Potter/Liner	9.94m	Falmouth
p	FH494	Son-A-Mor	Netter/Liner	6.2m	Coverack
p	FH496	Craggan	Potter	7.8m	Brixham
p	FH506	Silver Lance	Netter	5.6m	St Ives
p	FH508	Britannia IV	Netter/Liner	10.7m	Newlyn
p	FH529	Kingfisher II	Potter	7.8m	Cadgwith
	FH535	Gonpez I	Trawler	32.2m	Spain
p	FH597	Boy Brad	Netter	4.8m	Porthallow
p	FH598	Girl Rachael	Trawler	9.9m	St Mawes
P	FH601	Marney Lunn	Netter/Potter	5.9m	Helford R.
	Ex FH604	Jib-Jab	De-registered	5.2m	
p	FH609	Domar	Angler	4.2m	Falmouth
	FH610	Catherine Anne		5.8m	Cadgwith
p	FH611	Sea Urchin	Liner	4.8m	Porthallow
p	FH613	Kerany	Liner	4.8m	Porthoustock
p	FH614	Boy Daniel	Liner	4.4m	Newlyn
p	Ex FH619	Seagull	De-registered		Porthallow
p	FH623	Benediction	Netter/Potter	5.9m	Portloe
p	FH625	Boy Jack II	Liner	4.5m	Plymouth
p	FH629	Kathryn Louise II	Potter	4.5m	The Lizard
p	FH636	Cornish Gem	Scalloper	9.5m	Plymouth
	FH638	Ela-J		6.8m	Ex Falmouth
	FH639	Three Girls		5.6m	Ex Brixham
p	FH646	Willow	Netter	4.7m	Falmouth
p	FH664	Amethyst	Scalloper	9.9m	Falmouth
p	Ex FH667	Antoinette	De-registered	6.1m	Porthoustock
	FH668	Lucky lady		4.4m	Ex Cadgwith
p	FH669	Maria 2	Netter	7.1m	Falmouth
	FH671	Mary		4.5m	Ex Porthoustock
p	FH672	Kaisa Mari	Angler	5.1m	Teignmouth
	FH673	Greenwich	Trawler	35m	Spain
p	FH677	New Dawn	Potter/Liner	9.9m	Falmouth
	FH683	Blithe Spirit		5.2m	Falmouth
p	FH686	Rose	Potter	4.8m	Portscatho
p	FH690	Peter John II	Netter	8.0m	Falmouth

p	FH691	Bob Winnie	Netter	5.8m	Cadgwith
p	FH693	Lizy	Netter	9.97m	Mevagissey
p	FH697	Sweet Promise	Trawler	8.2m	Falmouth
	FH700	Rebecca		4.9m	Newlyn
	Ex FH701	Garfield Jean	De-registered	5.5m	Mullion
p	FH702	Cornish Lass	Liner	8.25m	Falmouth
p	FH704	Ruben Luke	Net/Pot/Liner	6.08m	Helford River
p	FH705	Hobbit	Netter	5.38m	Falmouth
p	FH706	Victoria Ann	Netter	5.9m	Cadgwith
	FH710	Abeko	Netter	26.6m	Spain
	FH711	Bluebell		4.94m	Ex Portloe
p	FH712	Zephron	Liner	4.8m	Portloe
p	FH714	Frances B	Netter/Potter	7.29m	Falmouth
p	FH715	Kimberley Jo	Netter/Potter	6.58m	Falmouth
p	FH716	Ruby Tuesday	Potter	4.61m	St Mawes
p	FH717	Cornish Lass IV	Potter	4.89m	Coverack
p	FH722	Prophet	Potter	6.85m	Falmouth
p	FH723	Harvester II	Netter/Potter	11.83m	Falmouth
p	FH728	Sterennyk	Netter/Liner	9.95m	Helford R.
p	FH730	Fiona Starr	Netter	<10m	Falmouth
	FR	**Fraserburgh**			
p	FR59	Golden Gain V	Trawler	25.7m	Visitor
p	FR317	Ocean Quest	Trawler	14.95m	Visitor
p	FR347	Ocean Dawn	Pair Trawler	26.5m	Visitor
p	FR359	Sunrise	Pair Seiner	26m	Visitor
p	FR821	Silver Star	Ring Netter	18m	Visitor
p	FR894	Ocean Star	Trawler	14.95m	Visitor
p	FR927	Propitious	Trawler	9.99	Brixham
p	FR951	Carisanne II	Trawler	23.0m	Visitor
	FY	**Fowey**			
p	FY1	Three Jays	Netter/Potter	4.78m	Gorran Haven
p	FY3	Storm Child	Liner	7.2m	Plymouth
p	FY4	Fulmar	Netter	4.87m	Gorran Haven
p	Ex FY7	Our Daddy	Sailing Ketch	14m	Looe
p	Ex FY12	Georgie Girl	De-registered	9.9m	Newlyn
p	FY15	Morvina	Angler	7.3m	Mevagissey

p	FY17	Kingfisher of Looe	Trawler	10.3m	Mevagissey
p	FY19	Christine	Liner	6.7m	Mevagissey
p	FY23	Little Pearl	Netter	9.98m	Newlyn
p	FY24	Ella	Trawler	11.3m	Looe
p	FY26	Ocean Queen	Netter	8.3m	Polperro
p	FY29	Little Fisher	Net/Pot/Liner	8.8m	Mevagissey
p	FY30	Vesper II	Netter	6.5m	Mevagissey
p	FY38	Maxine's Pride	Trawl/ Potter	11.9m	Looe
p	Ex FY41	Ar Tom	De-registered	5.6m	Looe
p	FY43	Lenten Rose	Trawler	9.98m	Mevagissey
p	FY44	Norvik	Potter/Liner	7.9m	Looe
p	FY46	Innisfallen	Trawler	9.98m	Newlyn
	FY47	Our Liz	Out of Area	8.7m	Ex St Ives
p	Ex FY51	Esther Jayne	Now FY870	5.5m	Polperro
p	FY53	Demelza	Netter	8.2m	Mevagissey
p	FY58	Venus	Netter	9.95m	Mevagissey
p	FY59	Swallow	Angler	11.7m	Looe
p	FY63	Kerry Jane	Netter/Potter	9.1m	Mevagissey
	FY64	Jolie Brise	Out of Area	10.0m	North Shields
p	FY66	Lucy Too	Netter	10.9m	Looe
p	FY71	Britannia II	Netter	6.5m	Mevagissey
p	FY88	Buccaneer	Netter	8.4m	Mevagissey
	Ex FY90	Lisa K	De-registered	5.9m	
p	FY95	Cristal Waters (Ex Virgo Lady)	Trawler/ Scalloper	9.99m	Plymouth
p	FY96	Aquamanda	Netter	8.1m	St Ives
p	FY97	Galatea	Trawler	12.0m	Looe
p	FY101	Emma Louise (Ex Susan 1)	Potter	6.4m	Looe
	Ex FY105	Callisto	De-registered	7.9m	
p	FY111	Red Vixen	Netter/Potter	10.4m	Mevagissey
p	FY115	Kessenyans	Netter/Liner	12.3m	Looe
p	Ex FY118	Cousin Jack	De-registered	5.9m	Ex Looe
p	FY119	Resolute	Ring Netter	9.95m	Mevagissey
p	FY120	Sirene	Netter	6.5m	Looe
p	FY126	Heather Anne	Netter	11.0m	Mevagissey

ALPHANUMERICAL INDEX by REGISTRATION NUMBER

p	Ex FY127	Erin	Lugsail Ketch		Looe
p	FY138	Ma-Gondole	Netter/Potter	8.8m	Padstow
p	Ex FY141	Our Trio	De-registered	4.5m	Ex Looe
	FY149	Palatine	Out of Area	9.95m	Lyme Regis
p	FY156	Charm	Potter	5.6m	Mevagissey
	Ex FY157	Penare II	De-registered	6.5m	Port Mellon
p	FY162	Bunowen	Liner/Angler	7.9m	Mevagissey
p	FY167	Coral Reef	Potter	5.7m	Porthleven
p	Ex FY173	May Queen	De-registered	9.6m	River Tamar
p	FY174	Emblem	Potter	4.6m	Gorran Haven
p	FY180	Katie Lil	Netter	5.9m	Portloe
	Ex FY183	Sonny Boy	De-registered	7.3m	Mevagissey
p	FY195	Maid of Boddinick	Potter	6.3m	Padstow
p	Ex FY221	Our Boys	Sail Ketch	14m	Looe
	FY224	Didier Patrice	Not in Use	15m	
p	FY226	Nor'Rocker	Netter/Potter	9.75m	Falmouth
p	FY228	Orca (Ex Reefer)	Potter	6.3m	Portwrinkle
p	Ex FY229	Coral	De-registered	5.4m	Hayle
p	Ex FY238	Frances	De-registered	13.7m	Ex Mevagissey
p	FY239	Lucy Marianna	Potter	9.14m	Helford R.
p	FY242	Cornish Maid Looe	Netter	5.9m	Downderry
p	FY254	Renown	Liner	6.8m	Mevagissey
p	FY269	Levan-Mor of Looe	Trawler	10.8m	Looe
p	FY270	Radjel	Netter	6.6m	Mevagissey
p	FY276	Zadok	Netter	9.9m	Plymouth
p	FY278	Puffin	Trawl/Liner	7.4m	Mevagissey
p	Ex FY290	Deu Kerens	Sailing Yawl	13m	Looe
p	FY292	Ibis	Liner	5.2m	Mevagissey
p	FY296	Islander	Angler	6.6m	Polperro
p	FY302	Lisanne of Looe	Netter/Potter	9.75m	Looe
p	FY303	Dispatcher	Crabber	6.1m	Looe
	FY304	Neptune's Bride		4.8m	Looe
p	Ex FY315	Shelley Jane	De-registered	7.5m	Mevagissey
p	FY324	Aquila	Netter/Potter	9.4m	Mevagissey
p	FY332	Tamara	Netter/Liner	8.5m	Mevagissey
p	FY345	Liver Bird	Netter	6.4m	Mevagissey
p	Ex FY362	Paula III	De-registered	9.1m	Looe

p	FY367	Investor (Ex WY36)	Scalloper	9.98m	Mevagissey
p	FY369	Paravel	Trawler	10.9m	Looe
p	Ex FY382	Lindy Lou	De-registered		Falmouth
p	FY399	Blue Marlin	Netter	9.45m	Fowey
p	FY400	Mako	Liner	8.0m	Mevagissey
p	FY424	Huntress	Netter	8.7m	Mevagissey
p	FY425	Southwind	Angler	7.3m	Mevagissey
p	FY431	Liberty	Net/Lin/Angler	8.1m	Mevagissey
p	Ex FY456	Lady Betty II	De-registered	9.1m	Padstow
p	Ex FY473	Bekidil	De-registered		Exmouth
p	FY509	Superb II	Netter	8.53m	Mevagissey
p	Ex FY519	Ibis	'Dandy' Ketch	12.2m	River Tamar
p	FY523	Mordros	Netter	9.23m	Mevagissey
p	FY527	Blejan Eyhre	Netter	11.95m	Newlyn
p	FY528	Andoray of Looe	Netter	7.7m	Fowey
p	FY529	Vesta	Netter	7.1m	Fowey
p	Ex FY531	Hickie	De-registered		Fowey
p	FY537	Anjo	Angler	9.3m	Looe
p	FY545	Jenny James	Netter	3.8m	Gorran Haven
p	FY555	Lyonesse	Potter	7.1m	Mevagissey
p	EX FY562	Progress	De-registered	8.5m	Looe
p	FY566	Karan	Potter	7.8m	St Ives
p	FY569	Marion	Potter	4.4m	Looe
p	FY570	Silvery Sea	Netter	9.6m	Helford R.
p	Ex FY575	Susie	De-registered	5.0m	Ex Looe
p	Ex FY576	Natalie Clare	De-registered	6.58m	Falmouth
p	FY578	C.H.E.A	Angler	5.6m	Mevagissey
p	FY583	Northern Star II	Netter	7.8m	Polperro
p	FY588	Boy Joe II	Liner	4.8m	Mevagissey
p	FY602	Natalie	Trawler	11.4m	Looe
p	FY614	Cazadora	Trawler	10.8m	Polperro
	Ex FY617	Pyscador	Now FY846	4.7m	Mevagissey
	Ex FY629	Sea Ranger	De-registered	9.4m	
p	FY661	Bellerophon	Out of Area	9.7m	Ex Looe
p	Ex FY662	Cornish Maid	De-registered	5.6m	Looe

p	Ex FY664	Petit Mickael	De-registered	15.6m	Fowey
	Ex FY701		De-registered		
p	FY755	Girl Amanda	Potter	6.2m	Looe
p	FY759	Surprise	Netter	6.72m	Mevagissey
p	FY764	Boy William	Potter	6.3m	Fowey
p	FY765	Little Anne	Potter	4.9m	Mevagissey
p	FY767	Neptunes Pride II	Potter	7.1m	Looe
p	Ex FY768	Mystique (Ex Looe)	De-registered	9.9m	Newquay
p	Ex FY773	Cara Mor	De-registered	5.6m	Teignmouth
p	FY776	Trewartha	Netter	6.0m	Mevagissey
p	FY777	Charltown	Net/Pot /Line	8.1m	Charlestown
p	FY778	Tanegan Ex Sirene	Netter/Potter	6.4m	Looe
p	FY781	Linda B	Netter	6.7m	Newlyn
	Ex FY783	Blue Diamond	De-registered	5.5m	
	FY787	Grandad		5.5m	
p	FY797	Pimpernel II	Netter	4.8m	Mevagissey
p	FY803	Verona (Ex Wave II)	Angler	5.4m	Mevagissey
p	FY804	Phoenix	Net/Crabber	9.98m	Looe
p	Ex FY806	Trya	De-registered	8.8m	Ex Looe
p	FY807	Jessica Grace	Trawler	9m	Fowey
	FY808	Francis Flo		7.2m	Ex Looe
	Ex FY809	Lady Amy	De-registered	4.9m	
p	FY811	Mary Eileen	Liner	4.8m	Mevagissey
p	FY813	Valiant	Netter	6.4m	Mevagissey
p	FY814	Arrant	Trawler	9.99m	Looe
p	FY817	Sammy Jayne	Potter	4.8m	Mevagissey
p	FY822	Fair Wind	Netter	7.3m	Polperro
p	FY823	Conway	Liner	4.7m	Mevagissey
p	FY824	Girl Bryher	Netter	5.8m	Newlyn
p	FY825	Swiftsure	Out of Area	9.8m	Ex Looe
p	FY826	Sunshine	Netter/Liner	6.4m	Mevagissey
p	FY827	Greta's Girl Ex Cornish Lass II	Out of Area	8.9m	Arbroath Ex Fowey
p	FY829	Ruby	Potter	4.5m	Gorran Haven
p	FY830	Atlantis	Trawler	9.9m	Looe

p	ExFY832	Izaak	De-registered	4.5m	Mevagissey
p	FY834	Katie's Pride	Netter	5.5m	Charlestown
	Ex FY835	Cawte 1	De-registered	6.4m	Ex Mevagissey
p	FY836	Lauren Kate	Netter	9.95m	Mevagissey
p	FY837	Jimini K	Liner	3.9m	Mevagissey
p	FY838	Boys Own 2	Angler	5.9m	Polperro
p	FY839	Katytu	Netter	6m	Looe
p	Ex FY840	Sumita	De-registered	7.5m	Polperro
p	FY841	Demper	Netter	4.88m	Mevagissey
p	FY843	Lucy B	Netter	4.3m	Mevagissey
p	FY846	Bella Margaret (Ex Pyscador)	Liner (Ex FY617)	4.6m	Mevagissey
p	FY847	Carlee	Potter (Cat)	8m	Looe
p	FY848	Defiant	Trawler	13.95m	Mevagissey
p	FY850	Typhoon	Netter	9.95m	Looe
p	FY852	Bethie Ann	Dive Boat	4.0m	Charlestown
p	Ex FY853	Finn-Lou	De-registered	6.4m	Ex Looe
p	Ex FY854	Viking Girl	De-registered	7.92m	Ex Polperro
p	FY857	Ocean Blue	Potter/Liner	9.95m	Looe
p	Ex FY859	Callisto	De-registered	7.78m	Mevagissey
p	FY860	Pania	Angler	6.2m	Looe
p	Ex FY862	Our Sophie	De-registered	7.9m	Looe
p	FY863	Temeraire	Netter	9.83m	Looe
p	FY864	Black Pearl	Netter/Liner	6.54m	Mevagissey
p	FY865	Helen Clare	Netter	4.45m	Charlestown
p	FY866	Cornish Lass III	Netter	9.98m	Fowey
p	Ex FY867	Kingfisher	De-registered	7.62m	Polperro
p	FY868	Cornishman	Liner	5.8m	Mevagissey
p	FY869	Mystique II	Netter/Liner	9.9m	Looe
p	FY870	Esther Jayne	Potter (Ex FY51)	5.5m	Polperro
p	FY872	Morgelyn	Netter	6.1m	Mevagissey
	FY873	Saturn III		4.65m	Mevagissey
	GE	**Goole**			
	GH	**Grangemouth**			
	GK	**Greenock**			
	GN	**Granton**	**(Edinburgh)**		
	GU	**Guernsey**			

ALPHANUMERICAL INDEX by REGISTRATION NUMBER

p	Ex GU74	Maraudeus(Ex BM192)	De-registered	15.19m	Visitor
p	GU116	Amy Blue (Ex C282)	Netter	14.63m	Visitor
	GW	**Glasgow**			
	GY	**Grimsby**			
p	GY165	Pacemaker	Scalloper	16.6m	Ilfracombe
p	GY341	Iysha	Netter	18.8m	Visitor
	H	**Hull**			
p	H105	Excelsior	Netter	9.9m	Plymouth
p	H145	Swift	Potter	9.99m	Hayle
p	H1074	Natalie B	Scalloper	26.5m	Visitor
	HH	**Harwich**			
p	HH76	Osprey	Netter/Potter	6.7m	Penzance
	HL	**Hartlepool**			
p	HL125	Boy Scott (Ex Chatterbox)	Netter	6.4m	Plymouth Ex Mevagissey
p	HL1054	Suvera	Trawler	9.8m	Brixham
p	HL1059	Cyclone	Netter	8.1m	Newquay
p	HL1061	Girl Emma	Netter/Potter	6.4m	Plymouth
	IE	**Irvine**			
	IH	**Ipswich**			
p	IH23	Our Steph	Trawler	9.2m	Brixham
p	IH68	Laura Anne	Potter	7.3m	River Yealm
p	IH180	Band of Hope	Netter	9.9m	Newquay
	INS	**Inverness**			
	ExINS154	Diadem	De-registered	18.2m	Ex Padstow
p	INS292	Courageous III	Pair Seiner	26m	Visitor
	J	**Jersey**			
	J86	Fleur de France	Potter	19.13m	Visitor
p	Ex J192	Pieterje	De-registered	26.2m	Ex Plymouth
p	Ex J217	Frances of Ladram	De-registered	22.2m	Plymouth
p	Ex J219	Evert Marutje	Motor Yacht	26.4m	River Tamar
p	J235	Kerloch	Potter	17.3m	Visitor
p	Ex J347	Grietje	De-registered	31.7m	Brixham Ex Plymouth
p	Ex J535	Pieter	De-registered	26.0m	Ex Plymouth
p	J612	La Vagabonde	Potter	17.7m	Teignmouth
	K	**Kirkwall**			
	Ex K779	Heather	De-registered	12.2m	Newlyn
p	K1126	Ceol Na Mar (Ex Sarah Jayne)	Whelker	11.0m	Appledore
	KY	**Kirkaldy**			
p	KY81	Comely II	Potter	7.6m	Mevagissey
p	KY115	Flourish	Trawl/Scallop	9.7m	Exmouth
p	Ex KY467	Three Boys	De-registered	9.9m	Exmouth
p	KY1001	Blue Diamond (Ex Charisma)	Potter	6.44m	Newlyn
	LA	**Llanelli**			
p	LA604	Silver Fish (Ex Skipper's Wife)	Out of Area	4.8m	Ex Dartmouth
	LH	**Leith**			
	LI	**Littlehampton**			
p	LI79	Sandella	Potter	7.3m	Exmouth
p	LI535	Alk I I	Potter	4.9m	Torquay
	LK	**Lerwick**			
p	LK37	Renown	Netter	18.07m	Padstow
	LL	**Liverpool**			
p	LL271	Dolphin	Scalloper	9.8m	Plymouth
	LN	**Kings Lynn**			
	LO	**London**			
p	LO59	Girl Linda	Trawler	9.85m	Hayle
p	LO540	Banana Split	Netter	6.2m	Porthoustock
	LR	**Lancaster**			
	LT	**Lowestoft**			
p	LT1	Our Boy Andrew	Trawler	10.0m	Looe
p	LT22	Sophie Dawn	Netter/Potter	9.98m	Ex Brixham
p	LT61	Sea Spray	Netter	9.9m	Newlyn
p	LT70	Emily Rose	Trawler	9.9m	Dartmouth
p	Ex LT266	Srenex Fidelis	Beam Trawler	25.5m	Ex Brixham

ALPHANUMERICAL INDEX by REGISTRATION NUMBER

p	LT278	Rose Dawn	Out of Area	6.0m	Ex Mevagissey
p	Ex LT526	Mareverma	De-registered	26.8m	Brixham
p	LT535	Korenbloem	Beam Trawler	27.5m	Brixham
p	LT976	Fenlander	Potter	6.2m	Port Isaac
p	LT1015	Glad Rags	Netter	7.6m	Fowey
	M	**Milford Haven**			
p	M8	Danmark	Trawler	9.8m	Penzance
p	M11	Torri Gwnt	Netter	4.8m	St Ives
p	M65	Sunstar	Potter	8.53m	Scilly
p	M78	Compass Rose II	Whelker	11.0m	Ilfracombe
p	M126	Clairvoyant	Netter/Liner	8.96m	Helford R.
p	Ex M313	Foxy Lady	De-registered	9.0m	Ex Plymouth
p	M560	Dignity	Netter	7.9m	Plymouth
p	M1141	Lucy	Potter	5.6m	Brixham
	ME	**Montrose**	**Methil**		
	MH	**Middlesborough**			
	ML	**Methil**	**(Fife)**		
p	Ex ML113	Storm Child	BM5 Brixham	10.0m	Ex Polperro
	MN	**Maldon**			
p	MN199	Solstice	Scalloper	9.9m	Mevagissey
	MR	**Manchester**			
	MT	**MaryPort**			
	N	**Newry**	**(Ireland)**		
	NN	**Newhaven**			
p	Ex NN88	Selina Ann	De-registered	10.9m	Plymouth
p	NN94	Semper Fidelis	Potter	8.1m	Newlyn
p	NN95	Chrissann	Netter	4.9m	Porthleven
p	NN137	Joanna	Trawler	14.0m	Looe
p	NN138	Aleyna	Trawl/Scallop	13.5m	Brixham
p	NN147	Duchess	Netter	9.14m	Appledore
p	NN257	Carina	Trawl/Scallop	14.0m	Brixham
p	NN722	Guiding Light II (Ex Alena)	Scalloper	13.4m	Looe
p	NN734	Winter's Tale	Trawler	9.8m	Appledore
	NS	**New Ross**	**(Ireland)**		

	NT	**NewPort**	**(Gwent)**		
p	NT28	Sea Pie	Trawler	9.9m	Visitor
	OB	**Oban**			
P	OB2	Prospect	Scalloper	9.98m	Exmouth
p	Ex OB61	Morning Glory	De-registerec	11.6m	Looe
p	OB89	Braveheart	Scalloper	9.9m	Falmouth
p	OB146	Mistress III	Netter/Potter	9.9m	Newquay
p	OB254	Virgo	Trawl/Scallop	15.08	Brixham
p	OB324	Bridie May	Potter	9.3m	Hayle
p	OB438	Feusgan	Potter	7.65m	Brixham
p	OB454	Kelley Marena	Trawler	9.99m	Brixham
	P	**Portsmouth**			
p	P29	Equinox	Trawler/Netter	11.9m	Mevagissey
p	P483	Ability	Trawler	11.5m	Mevagissey
p	P940	Dawn Raider	Netter	9.9m	Polperro
p	P965	Lady Claire	Out of Area	9.9m	Ex Newlyn
	PD	**Peterhead**			
p	PD220	Aquila	Trawler	21.8m	Visitor
p	PD313	Rosemount	Pair Seiner	26m	Visitor
p	PD905	Honeybourne III	Scalloper	29.16m	Newlyn
p	PD959	Demares	Pair Seiner	24.4m	Visitor
	PE	**Poole**			
p	PE477	Anthon	Netter	6.14m	Plymouth
p	PE487	Libra Lass	Potter	7.2m	Brixham
p	PE310	Ben Thomas	Trawler	9.9m	Fowey
p	Ex PE524	Endeavour	De-registered	8m	Plymouth
p	PE820	Avon Valley	Trawl/Scallop	12.3m	St Mawes
p	PE888	Lady Matilda	Netter	9.2m	Helford River
	PGW	**Port Glasgow**			
	PH	**Plymouth**			
p	PH2	Secret Star	Angler	8m	Plymouth
p	PH9	Girl Gillian	Potter	7.5m	Falmouth
p	Ex PH10	Sepia	Dive Boat	12.3m	Plymouth
p	PH11	KSH	Potter	9.2m	River Tamar

ALPHANUMERICAL INDEX by REGISTRATION NUMBER

p	PH12	Carla May	Potter	7.2m	Plymouth
p	PH24	Su Jean	Trawler	9.8m	Padstow
p	PH25	Sula Bassana	Net/Potter/Liner	8.2m	River Tamar
p	PH34	Tamesis II	Angler	10m	Plymouth
p	Ex PH48	Lancer	De-registered	7.2m	Plymouth
p	PH58	Bruno of Sutton	Trawler	15.1m	Bideford
p	PH60	Warrior	Angler	9.5m	Plymouth
P	PH74	On Ward	Netter/Potter	5.64m	Falmouth
p	PH76	Raven	Angler	6.9m	River Tamar
p	Ex PH79	Sweet Home	De-registered	7m	Plymouth
p	PH82	Neptune	Angler	4.4m	Portwrinkle
p	ExPH90	Squilla	De-registered	19.7m	Ex Plymouth
p	Ex PH98	Kittiwake	De-registered	9m	Ex Plymouth
p	PH99	Franjo A	Trawler	11.4m	Plymouth
p	PH101	Snowdrop	Liner	5.7m	Teignmouth
	PH104	Boy Scott		8.0m	Ex Newquay
p	PH110	Wiron 1	Pelagic Trawler	51.4m	Plymouth
p	PH115	Sat Rat	Potter	9.2m	River Tamar
p	PH117	Trio	Angler	9.6m	Plymouth
	Ex PH121	Cornish Bird	De-registered		Ex Padstow
p	PH122	Bosloe	Trawl/Net/Pot	14.4m	Plymouth
p	PH160	Compass Rose	Potter	8.2m	Plymouth
p	Ex PH167	Anderton Lady	De-registered	7.1m	Ex Plymouth
p	Ex PH207	Gammarus	De-registered		Plymouth
p	PH220	Wiron 2	Pelagic Trawler	51.4m	Plymouth
p	Ex PH221	Jontine	De-registered	6.1m	Plymouth
p	Ex PH224	Western Enterprise	De-registered		Plymouth
p	PH245	Pauline J	Out of Area	10m	Ex Plymouth
p	PH254	Brenda C	Potter	9.3m	Plymouth
p	PH271	Kelly J	Angler	7.3m	Plymouth
p	PH277	Chiltern Boy	Potter	7.5m	Plymouth
p	Ex PH299	Flying Freckles	De-registered	7.2m	Plymouth
p	PH307	Splendour	Netter/Angler	7.5m	Plymouth
p	PH316	Darter	Netter	9.8m	Plymouth

p	PH320	(Un named)	Not Registered	<10m	River Tamar
p	PH322	Metan	Potter/Liner	8.3m	Plymouth
p	PH326	Moby Dick	Trawler/Netter	9.2m	Teignmouth
p	PH330	Admiral Gordon	Beam Trawler	22.1m	Plymouth
p	PH344	Jessie Lou	Scalloper	12.5m	Plymouth
p	PH350	Samphire	Angler	7.2m	Plymouth
p	PH356	Scathmas	Potter	4.4m	Portwrinkle
p	PH381	Dionne	Trawl/Net/Pot/Line	7.8m	Newquay
	PH400	Willing Boys	Trawler	29.2m	Troon
p	PH411	Silver Stream	Trawler	14.5m	Plymouth
p	PH429	Shelley Marie	Trawler	11.6m	Plymouth
p	Ex PH431	Cavio-Tan	De-registered	6m	Ex Plymouth
p	PH440	Admiral Blake	Beam Trawler	22.3m	Plymouth
p	Ex PH452	Sherlmar	SANK Aug 2005	10.3m	Ex Plymouth
p	Ex PH463	Tiburon	De-registered	9m	Plymouth
p	Ex PH473	Swift	De-registered	5.4m	Dartmouth
p	PH477	Hooker	Angler	8.0m	Clovelly
p	Ex PH487	Verity	De-registered	5m	Salcombe
p	Ex PH491	Amoco	De-registered	10m	Plymouth
p	PH530	Katrina	Netter/Potter/Liner /Oyster Drag	6.4m	Plymouth
p	PH550	Admiral Grenville	Beam Trawler	24m	Plymouth
p	PH564	Isabella	Netter/Potter	6.8m	Plymouth
	Ex PH565	Jodi-P	De-registered	<10m	
p	PH571	Cheryl Diana (Ex Fiona Grace)	Netter/Potter	7.3m	River Tamar
p	PH572	My Girls	Netter/Potter	7.8m	Polperro
p	PH574	Kinsman	Trawler	10m	Plymouth
p	PH575	Duet	Angler	9m	River Tamar
p	Ex PH579	Tiddler	De-registered	7.4m	Ex Plymouth
p	PH583	Surf Hunter	Netter/Potter	7.2m	Newquay
p	PH584	Our Louise	Netter	9.6m	Bridlimgton
p	PH585	Shiralee/Plymouth	Crabber	8.2m	River Tamar
p	PH586	Gwalarn	Scalloper	10m	Plymouth

p	PH587	Belle Etoile	Scalloper	9.3m	Plymouth
p	PH588	La Coquet	Potter	7.45m	Falmouth
p	PH589	Maverick	Angler	9.5m	Plymouth
	Ex PH597	Starlight	De-registered	12m	Ex Plymouth
p	PH598	Lisa Leanne	Scalloper	9.6m	Plymouth
p	PH650	Northern Lass	Potter	7.4m	Plymouth
p	PH959	Richard Ann	Trawler/Netter	9.99m	Plymouth
p	PH961	Lady Jane (2005 Merlin)	Out of Area (Now LK780)	9.99m	Ex Plymouth
p	Ex PH962	D J	De-registered	9.95m	Ex Plymouth
p	PH989	Barbican Lady	Stern Trawl	9.9m	Plymouth
p	PH990	Barbican Maid	Scalloper	9.9m	Newlyn
p	ExPH5546	Albatross	De-registered	8.9m	Ex Brixham
	PH5547	Our Roseanne		10m	
p	PH5557	Emma Louise	Netter	9.9m	Plymouth
	ExPH5559	Le Cou Cou	De-registered	10m	Ex Brixham
p	PH5561	Katherine M	Trawler	10m	Plymouth
p	PH5562	Helcon	Trawler	10m	Appledore
p	PH5568	Challenge	Netter	8m	River Yealm
p	PH5573	Harrier	Potter	6.5m	Plymouth
p	Ex PH5575	Lark	De-registered	6m	Plymouth
p	PH5576	Shell Belle	Angler	5m	River Tamar
p	PH5577	My Diane	Angler	6m	Plymouth
p	PH5578	Petit Folie	Scalloper	8m	Plymouth
p	ExPH5579	Ocean Breeze	De-registered	9m	Ex Plymouth
p	PH5583	Hannah Jack	Netter	9.83m	Plymouth
p	ExPH5584	Lindora	De-registered	8m	Ex R. Tamar
p	PH5585	New Dawn xGU360	Trawler	11.4m	Brixham
p	PH5586	Moonraker	Potter	8.7m	River Tamar
p	PH5587	Bounty	Netter	8.0m	Plymouth
p	PH5590	Fair Trade Ex LI133	Netter/Potter	7.01m	Plymouth
	PL	**Peel (I.O.M.)**			
p	PL8	Two Girls	Trawler		IoM
	PN	**Preston**			
	PO	**Portland**			
	PT	**Port Talbot**			
	PW	**Padstow**			
p	PW1	Berlewen	Netter	14.97m	Padstow
	PW4	Marlene		4.46m	Ex Boscastle
	Ex PW5	Sabre of Newquay	De-registered	9.7m	Newlyn
p	PW9	Celtic Mor	Netter	7.95m	Padstow
p	PW10	Emma Kate II	Angler	9.88m	Padstow
p	Ex PW11	Emma Kate	De-registered	8.8m	Teignmouth
p	Ex PW13	Plover	De-registered	6.8m	Padstow
	PW14	Charlotte Nancy	Scalloper	23m	Buckie
p	PW20	Janice Mary	Angler	6.0m	Padstow
p	PW23	Sarafina Ex Laura B	Netter/Potter	7.2m	Scilly
p	PW32	Cornish Gem	Potter	8.4m	Plymouth
	PW33	Diana Marion		6.5m	Port Isaac
p	PW36	Le Loustic	Angler	5.9m	Padstow
p	PW37	Amy O	Netter	4.85m	Padstow
	PW56	Daring		5.2m	Ex Port Isaac
p	PW60	Little Pearl	Potter	4.9m	Salcombe
p	PW64	Trevose/Newquay	Netter	12.44m	Newlyn
p	Ex PW68	(Un-named)	De-registered	<5m	Port Gaverne
p	PW75	Palores	Netter	7.9m	Polperro
p	PW77	Girl Rachel	Potter	9.95m	Padstow
p	PW81	Julie Girl	Netter/Liner	8.2m	Helford River
p	PW95	Eleanor Roget	Potter	10.1m	Padstow
p	Ex PW96	Jan B	De-registered	7.32m	Lynmouth
p	PW100	Our Belle Ann	Potter	11.7m	Port Isaac
p	PW104	Sharicmar	Netter/Potter	8.2m	Port Isaac
	PW105	Pisces II		4.9m	Ex Port Isaac
p	PW107	Tallula	Potter	9.3m	Newquay

ALPHANUMERICAL INDEX by REGISTRATION NUMBER

	Ex PW111	Arkle	De-registered	6.5m	Ex Port Isaac
p	PW122	Zarvan	Netter/Potter	8.1m	Newquay
p	PW124	Helen Jane II	Netter	9.83m	Padstow
p	PW132	Boscastle Belle	Potter	8.5m	Padstow
p	PW150	Jean Howard	Trawler	11.2m	Appledore
p	PW160	Fiona Mary	Netter	9.99m	Brixham
p	Ex PW182	M C B	De-registered	8.6m	Ex Polperro
p	Ex PW184	Island Ranger	De-registered		West Bay
p	PW186	Shiela Pat	Potter	8.1m	Plymouth
p	Ex PW197	Lily May	De-registered	6.2m	Bude
p	PW201	La Conquete	Trawler	9.9m	Brixham
p	PW214	Thomas Andrew	Netter	9.83m	Padstow
p	PW228	Ma-Vie	Netter	8.74m	Helford River
p	PW235	Boy John II	Potter	5.3m	Port Isaac
p	PW240	Diligence	Potter	8.7m	Padstow
	PW242	Our Winnie		4.0m	Ex Port Isaac
p	PW287	Lady Di	Liner	6.6m	Portreath
p	PW289	Boscastle Peganina	Potter/Angler	10.05m	Boscastle
	Ex PW310	Mako III	De-registered	5.1m	Ex Padstow
p	PW333	Daymer Bay	Netter/Potter	8.0m	Padstow
	PW346	Sea Star		5.6m	Ex Newlyn
p	PW362	Charlotta	Scallop/Netter	7.98m	Mevagissey
p	PW364	Orcades II	Potter	12.2m	Port Isaac
p	PW371	Three J's	Netter/Potter	8.4m	Newquay
	Ex PW374	Oneida	De-registered	10.0m	Brixham
p	Ex PW377	Guiding Light	De-registered	11.9m	Ex Looe
p	PW392	Erindors	Netter	5.1m	Padstow
p	PW393	Winnie the Pooh	Potter	6.5m	Port Isaac
	Ex PW399	Potter	De-registered	4m	Ex Plymouth
	Ex PW404	Flying Fisher	De-registered	5.7m	Ex Port Isaac
p	Ex PW410	Linda J	De-registered	<10m	Bude
p	PW412	Helen Jane	Trawler/Netter	9.65m	Newquay
p	PW429	Helen Claire II	Potter	10.0m	Port Isaac
	Ex PW430	Girl Poppy	De-registered	5.7m	Ex Newquay
p	PW431	Mako of Bude	Potter	7.8m	Bude
p	PW432	Che Sara Sara	Potter/Angler	9.8m	Newquay

	PW433	Strike		4.9m	Ex Padstow
	Ex PW435	Ace of Spades	De-registered	5.6m	Ex Newquay
p	Ex PW436	Nicola J	De-registered	8.0m	Padstow
p	PW437	Early Bird	Netter	5.4m	Bude
	PW439	Donna Marie	Out of Area	7.2m	Ex Mevagissey
p	PW440	Finnish Girl	Angler	6.0m	Falmouth
	PW442	Long Shot	Out of Area	5.6m	Weymouth
p	PW443	Strike	Netter/Tender	5.1m	Exmouth
	PW445	Falcon		5.6m	Ex Padstow
p	PW446	Free Spirit	Potter	8.5m	Port Isaac
p	PW449	George-D	Netter	7.2m	Dartmouth
p	PW453	Doo Da Day	Liner	7.1m	Mousehole
p	PW455	Lenny P	Potter	4.93m	Port Gaverne
p	PW456	Lily May II	Potter/Liner	6.9m	Bude
p	Ex PW459	Dire Straits	De-registered	7.6m	Ex Plymouth
p	PW460	Blue Fox	Angler	8.2m	Padstow
p	PW461	Gwendra	Potter/Liner	4.96m	Scilly
p	PW463	Roams	Potter	4.84m	Port Gaverne
	PW469	For a Few Dollars More		6m	Hayle
p	PW470	Bon Amy	Potter	8.25m	Padstow
p	PW474	Jacqueline	Angler	<10m	Padstow
	PZ	**Penzance**	**(Newlyn)**		
p	PZ1	Fran Beth	Netter/Liner		Newlyn
p	Ex PZ1	3 Girls	De-registered		Sennen
p	Ex PZ1	Amanda J ExPZ9	De-registered	5.9m	Penzance
p	PZ2	Trident II	Potter	7.2m	Mousehole
	PZ3	We-re Here		3.2m	Ex Penzance
p	PZ4	Cormoran	Netter/Potter	6.2m	Marazion
p	Ex PZ5	Blue Fin	De-registered	5.58m	Newlyn
p	PZ5	Sou'wester	Liner	<5m	Newlyn
p	PZ6	Girl Pamela	Netter	11.5m	Newlyn
p	Ex PZ8	Grace	Lugsail Ketch	12.8m	Penzance
p	PZ8	The Boss	Liner	6.4m	Newlyn

ALPHANUMERICAL INDEX by REGISTRATION NUMBER

p	Ex PZ9	Isabelle	De-registered		Porthleven
p	PZ9	Morning Star	Netter(ExPZ21)	7.67m	Porthleven
p	Ex PZ10	Nellie	De-registered	26.2m	Ex Newlyn
p	PZ10	Nellie	Scalloper	22.2m	Newlyn
p	PZ12	Chancer	Potter	7.5m	Newlyn
p	PZ14	Sowenna	Netter	18.0m	Newlyn
p	PZ15	Spaven Mor	Potter	6.58m	Plymouth
	Ex PZ16	Anne Mary	De-registered	4.9m	West Bay
p	PZ17	Teal	Liner	4.45m	Lamorna Cove
	PZ20	Jenny		4.7m	Newlyn
p	PZ21	Pandora III	Netter	4.5m	Mousehole
p	PZ22	Sarah-M	Liner	5.9m	Newlyn
p	PZ23	Treen	Liner	4.9m	Newlyn
p	PZ25	White Rose	Liner	4.6m	Porthgwarra
p	PZ30	Loyal Partner	Netter/Potter	10.7m	Newquay
p	PZ32	Cathryn	Trawler	12.2m	Newlyn
p	PZ34	Emily	Liner		Newlyn
p	PZ39	Father Bob	Liner	4.6m	Penberth
p	PZ40	Gemma	Netter/Liner	6.5m	St Ives
p	PZ41	Ocean Spray	Netter	14.1m	Newlyn
	PZ43	Enigma (ExBoy Andrew)	Potter	5.9m	St Ives
p	PZ44	Amy Rose	Netter	4.8m	Coverack
p	PZ47	Lowena-Mor	Net/Pot /Liner	6.0m	Newlyn
p	PZ48	Lorraine Ruth	Potter	4.8m	Salcombe
p	PZ49	Treglown (ExLa Mouette)	Netter/Potter	7.9m	Hayle
p	PZ50	Ennis Lady (Ex Kingfisher)	Netter	7.5m	Porthleven
	PZ53	Sunrise	Liner	4.4m	Ex Penberth
p	Ex PZ54	Girl Frances	De-registered		Lizard
p	PZ57	Girl Patricia	Netter	17.8m	Newlyn
p	PZ61	Guiding Star	Netter	5.5m	NewlynExHayle
p	PZ62	Sea Fox	Netter/Liner	5.9m	Newlyn
p	PZ63	Golden Harvest	Netter	15.0m	Newlyn

p	PZ64	St Elvan	Potter	4.8m	Porthleven
	PZ65	Kindly Light		6.46m	Ex Porthleven
p	PZ66	Sapphire	Beam Trawler	25.05m	Newlyn
p	PZ68	Starfish	Liner/Angler	9.6m	Porthleven
p	PZ72	Lauran	Liner	4.8m	Newlyn
p	PZ74	Sanluro	Netter/Liner	6.21m	Newlyn
p	PZ75	William Harvey	Potter	12.64m	Newlyn
p	PZ77	Shelley Marie	Liner	5.92m	Newlyn
p	PZ78	James R H Stevenson	Beam Trawler	29.8m	Newlyn
p	PZ80	Anna Rosa	Liner	5.1m	Porthoustock
p	PZ82	Chicadee	Tender	7.0m	Newlyn
p	PZ84	Pen Kernow	Liner	4.5m	C. Cornwall
p	PZ85	Girl Kim	Potter/Liner	6.0m	Newlyn
p	PZ86	Spilgarn	Potter	4.5m	Portreath
p	PZ87	Katie Claire (Ex FD407)	Beam Trawler /Scalloper	13.45m	Newlyn
p	PZ88	Viking	Angler	9.6m	Penzance
p	PZ91	Clair	Liner	4.33m	Sennen
p	PZ98	Leader	Potter	5.5m	Newlyn
p	PZ99	Basil St Cl Stevenson	Beam Trawler	26.12m	Newlyn
p	ExPZ100	Semper Allegro	(Now J217)	25.22m	Ex Newlyn
p	PZ100	Elizabeth N	Beam Trawler	21.34m	Newlyn
p	ExPZ101	Children's Friend	Sail Lugger		Newlyn
p	ExPZ105	Constant	Private Yacht		Newlyn
	PZ109	Two Boys	De-registered	4.7m	Ex Newlyn
p	ExPZ110	Sea Hawk	De-registered	8.6m	Newlyn
p	PZ111	Veracity	Lugsail Ketch	9.8m	Dartmouth
p	PZ123	Sara Shaun	Beam Trawler	25.32m	Newlyn
p	PZ124	Minnow	Liner	4.1m	Hayle
p	PZ125	Patrice	Netter/Potter	8.0m	Mullion
p	ExPZ126	Bonnie	De-registered		Mousehole
	PZ130	Lone Wolf	Potter	8.9m	Newlyn
p	PZ137	Twilight III	Beam Trawler	29.1m	Newlyn
p	PZ140	Paul Arran	Netter	5.9m	St Ives
p	PZ146	Anna Catherine	Netter	4.4m	C. Cornwall

ALPHANUMERICAL INDEX by REGISTRATION NUMBER

p	ExPZ151		De-registered		Penberth
p	PZ155	Sarah Jane-T	Liner	4.6m	Newlyn
p	PZ166	Venture	Liner	5.5m	Newlyn
p	Ex PZ167	Lowenek	De-registered	4.9m	Mullion
	Ex PZ174	Wyvern	De-registered	4.6m	Newlyn
p	PZ179	Merbreeze	Netter	4.7m	(Ex Polperro) Newquay
p	PZ184	Ceres	Liner	6.7m	Newlyn
p	PZ190	Mathew Harvey	Netter/Potter	12.19m	Newlyn
p	PZ191	William S Stevenson	Beam Trawler	28.24m	Newlyn
p	PZ192	Jacqueline	Beam Trawler	23.7m	Newlyn
p	PZ193	Trevessa IV	Beam Trawler	26.15m	Newlyn
p	PZ194	Roseland	Trawler	23.61m	Newlyn
p	PZ195	William Stevenson	Beam Trawler	25.99m	Newlyn
p	PZ196	Trewarvaneth	Netter	23.29m	Newlyn
p	PZ197	Annaliese	Beam Trawler	26.21m	Newlyn
p	PZ198	Aaltje Adriaantje	Beam Trawler	28.6m	Newlyn
p	PZ199	Algrie	Beam Trawler	26.2m	Newlyn
p	PZ203	A B S	Beam Trawler	25.28m	Newlyn
p	PZ209	Tara	Liner	5.0m	Lamorna Cove
p	Ex PZ211	Pet	Lugsail		Falmouth
p	PZ212	Lee-Am	Liner	4.4m	Mousehole
p	PZ218	Sprigs of Heather	Liner	5.6m	Newlyn
p	Ex PZ233	I'll Try	De-registered	5.5m	Helford River
	Ex PZ242	Edward Harvey	De-registered	13.84m	Ex Newlyn
	Ex PZ245	Julian Paul	De-registered	15.03m	Ex Newlyn
p	PZ260	Princess Diane	Liner	7.0m	Porthleven
p	PZ272	White Heather	Netter	5.6m	St Ives
p	Ex PZ277	Pioneer	Gaff Ketch		Hayle
p	PZ280	Talisman	Netter/Liner	9.33m	Helford River
p	PZ290	Bryan D Stevenson	Beam Trawler	26.87m	Newlyn
p	PZ291	Elizabeth A Webster	Beam Trawler	29.88m	Newlyn
p	PZ293	Elizabeth Caroline	Beam Trawler	29.85m	Newlyn

p	PZ295	Marie Claire	Beam Trawler	29.85m	Newlyn
p	PZ302	Boy Adam	Netter	5.9m	Newlyn
p	PZ315	Tamsin T	Liner	5.5m	Newlyn
p	PZ317	Sea Spirit	Liner	6.5m	Newlyn
p	Ex PZ317	Bounders II	De-registered	8.2m	Penzance
p	PZ329	Harvest Reaper	Trawler	11.9m	Newlyn
p	PZ331	Anthony Stevenson	Netter	23.33m	Newlyn
p	PZ339	Cornish Lass	Tender	8.0m	Newlyn
	Ex PZ346	Bumble B II	De-registered	8.2m	Newlyn
p	PZ353	Girl Penny	Netter	9.9m	Newlyn
	Ex PZ371		De-registered		Ex Hayle
p	PZ379	Boy Harvey	Potter/Liner	7.7m	Hayle
	Ex PZ385	Lady Caroline	De-registered	5.6m	Newlyn
p	PZ395	Lisa	Tender	6.7m	Newlyn
p	Ex PZ403	Our Ocean Harvester	De-registered	17.6m	Newlyn
p	Ex PZ410	Sea Hunter	De-registered	5.2m	Newlyn
p	PZ425	CKS	Netter	16.73n	Newlyn
p	PZ428	Stergan	Liner	8.0m	Hayle
p	PZ436	Michael & David	Netter/Liner	11.1m	Newlyn
p	PZ437	Frances Rose	Netter/Liner	5.6m	Newlyn
p	PZ439	Lugi	Liner	4.48m	Newlyn
p	PZ453	Laurie Jean	Potter	5.6m	Scilly
	Ex PZ454	Suzie	De-registered	4.9m	St Ives
p	PZ457	Lily	Potter	5.0m	Mousehole
p	PZ459	Celtic Lass	Potter	9.9m	Falmouth
p	PZ462	Aylishia	Netter	5.0m	Porthallow
p	PZ475	Reliance	Potter	9.3m	Porthleven
p	PZ476	Lisa Jacquie Stevenson	Beam Trawler	24.2m	Newlyn
p	PZ477	Mary Rose	Liner	5.6m	Porthoustock
p	PZ478	Lyonesse ofCape	Liner	4.4m	C. Cornwall
p	PZ480	Kelyn Mor	Liner	4.6m	Newquay
p	PZ481	Vipa	Netter/Liner	5.6m	St Ives

p	Ex PZ482	Nampara	De-registered	<5m	Hayle
p	PZ490	Barry Ann	Potter	5.0m	Sennen
p	PZ495	Jackie Marie	Potter	5.1m	Mevagissey
	Ex PZ498	Lena I	De-registered	18.9m	Ex Newlyn
	PZ499	Twilight		8.0m	Ex Newlyn
p	PZ512	Cornishman	Beam Trawler	32.8m	Newlyn
p	PZ513	Excellent	Netter	24.8m	Newlyn
	Ex PZ518	Boy Anthony	De-registered	12m	
p	PZ520	Reward (Ex Harvest Home)	Netter	6.5m	St Ives
p	PZ527	Bass Boy	Netter	5.14m	Church Cove
p	PZ532	Billy Rowney	Beam Trawler	31.8m	Newlyn
p	PZ536	Gazelle	Liner	4.7m	Penberth
p	PZ540	Grey Seal	Liner	4.6m	Penberth
p	PZ542	Filadelfia	Beam Trawler	26.3m	Newlyn
p	PZ545	Sarah Ann	Netter	4.9m	Penzance
p	PZ550	Prue Esther II	Netter	11.6m	Newlyn
p	PZ557	Celtic Breeze	Potter/Liner	7.3m	Hayle
p	Ex PZ559	Silver Sides	De-registered	4.4m	C. Cornwall
p	PZ564	Tamara	Netter/Potter	4.5m	Sennen
p	Ex PZ570	Rachel Cara	De-registered	4.47m	C. Cornwall
p	PZ574	Flowing Tide	Potter	5.55m	Mullion
p	PZ575	Mary Frances	Angler	5.7m	Falmouth
p	PZ580	Aquilla	Netter/Liner	4.8m	Mousehole
p	PZ584	Butts	Netter/Liner	5.7m	Newlyn
p	PZ585	Curlew	Liner	4.8m	Penberth
p	PZ590	She Wolf	Netter/Liner	9.9m	Hayle
p	PZ592	Alice Louise	Netter/Potter	7.9m	Newlyn
	Ex PZ595		Lugsail Ketch		Dartmouth
p	PZ601	Fulmar	Potter	5.9m	Cadgwith
p	PZ611	Tan-Nos	Liner	4.5m	Newlyn
p	PZ612	Rachel & Paul	Potter/Liner	5.6m	Newlyn
p	PZ620	Carol & David	Liner	4.8m	Penberth
	Ex PZ622	Silver Harvester	De-registered	33.7	Ex Penzance
p	PZ631	Penver	Liner	4.6m	Penberth

p	PZ632	Macareux	Trawler	9.9m	Ilfracombe
	PZ638	Ro-Mi-Chris		4.9m	Newlyn
p	Ex PZ639	Girl Pearl	De-registered	7.2m	Porthleven
p	PZ641	Mark & James	Liner	5.5m	St Ives
p	PZ642	Serene	Netter	5.9m	Helford River
p	Ex PZ643	Gary-M	De-registered	11.87m	Newlyn
p	PZ645	Ben My Chree	Netter	17.25m	Newlyn
p	PZ654	Hicca	Liner	4.8m	Penberth
p	PZ663	Cynthia	Liner	5.6m	St Ives
	Ex PZ665	Marlin	De-registered	4.5m	Ex Sennen
	PZ674	Mouzel Dawn		6.2m	Ex St Ives
p	Ex PZ677	Salamanda	De-registered	6.9m	Porthleven
p	Ex PZ679	Acilla	De-registered	4.8m	Mousehole
p	PZ682	Helona	Liner	5.7m	Newlyn
p	PZ683	Lafrowda	Potter	5.9m	Portreath
p	PZ689	John Louise	Liner	4.8m	Newlyn
p	PZ695	Jade	Liner	5.9m	Hayle
p	PZ699	Boy Matt	Netter	4.9m	Sennen
p	PZ707	Scorpio	Netter/Potter	7.8m	Cadgwith
	Ex PZ711	Jackie G	De-registered	8.9m	Ex Newlyn
p	PZ715	Cares Lel	Liner	5.6m	Mevagissey
p	PZ718	Eel-Avum	Netter	5.0m	Penzance
p	PZ729	Pegasus	Potter	6.4m	Newlyn
p	PZ734	Cynth	Potter	4.5m	Scilly
p	PZ738	Our Margaret	Netter/Liner	5.6m	St Ives
p	Ex PZ747	Penny Lynn	De-registered	5.6m	Penberth
p	Ex PZ748	Cousin Jack	De-registered	6.5m	Falmouth
p	PZ753	Sarah C Stevenson	Beam Trawler	29.2m	Newlyn
p	PZ756	Charlotte Louise II	Netter	7.0m	Newlyn
p	Ex PZ758	Little Halcyon	De-registered	4.6m	Mousehole
p	PZ764	Boy Robert	Netter	4.7m	St Ives
p	PZ768	Onward	Liner	4.7m	Newlyn
p	PZ770	Pol Pry II	Netter	4.8m	Sennen
p	PZ771	Silenus	Netter	6.5m	Coverack

	Ex PZ772	Goldfinder	De-registered	11.9m	Ex Brixham
p	PZ775	Ocean Breeze	Liner	5.6m	Newlyn
p	PZ777	Gloria	Potter	4.4m	Sennen Cove
p	PZ778	Naomi G	Potter	4.5m	Clovelly
p	PZ779	Jack-Anny	Liner	4,7m	Newlyn
	PZ780	Karen Jane		4.8m	Ex Salcombe
	PZ781	Mourne Shore		8.2m	Ex Newquay
	Ex PZ783	Boy Mathew	De-registered	4.5m	Ex Newlyn
p	PZ800	Rebecca Ann	Liner	5.6m	Newlyn
p	PZ807	Sharker	Liner	4.9m	Mousehole
p	PZ810	Alvic	Liner	5.6m	Newlyn
p	PZ882	Sea Lion	Liner	5.1m	Newlyn
p	Ex PZ883	Prevail	De-registered	12.73m	Newlyn
p	PZ888	Utsker	Netter	9.99m	Newlyn
p	PZ890	Little Waters	Netter	11.28m	Newlyn
p	PZ903	Go-For-It	Netter	7.3m	Newlyn
	Ex PZ940	Ben Sayer Laxa	De-registered	9.9m	Ex Newlyn
p	Ex PZ957	Bee-Jay	De-registered		Newlyn
p	PZ999	Jannie en Klaas	Beam Trawler	26.15m	Newlyn
p	PZ1001	Resurgam	Beam Trawler	26.22m	Newlyn
p	PZ1015	Rachel & Victoria	Netter	5.6m	Plymouth
p	PZ1024	Ros-Na-Riogh	Netter	14.5m	Newlyn
p	PZ1053	St Georges	Beam Trawler	34.8m	Newlyn
p	PZ1172	Daisy Christianne	Trawler	39.1m	Newlyn
p	PZ1174	Edward J (Ex Ennis Lady)	Potter	6.5m	Boscastle
p	ExPZ1177	Jess	De-registered		Sennen
p	PZ1181	Maid Donna	Netter	9.1m	Porthleven
p	PZ1183	Pendower	Liner	5.6m	Newlyn
p	Ex PZ1184	Anne Louise	De-registered	6.3m	Newlyn
p	PZ1186	Chloet	Beam Trawler	26.2m	Newlyn
p	PZ1187	Girl Stella	Netter	6.38m	Hayle
p	PZ1188	Ophelia	Scalloper	9.6m	Falmouth
p	PZ1189	Jessica Ione	Netter	6.4m	Teignmouth
p	PZ1191	Sally Roseof Navax	Potter	7.3m	Hayle

p	PZ1193	Ellie Mae	Liner	6.7m	Newlyn
p	PZ1196	Silver Dawn	Netter	16.39m	Falmouth
p	PZ1197	Danni Rose	Liner	5.4m	St Ives
p	PZ1198	Golden Fleece	Potter	5.8m	Porthleven
p	PZ1199	Sea Goblin	Potter	4.9m	Sennen
p	PZ1200	Celtic Sunrise	Netter/Potter	5.94m	Mullion
p	PZ1201	Cachalot	Liner	7.35m	Hayle
p	PZ1202	GeminiTwo	Liner	4.79m	St Ives
p	PZ1209	Rose Bud	Potter/Liner	4.86m	Newlyn
p	PZ1212	Two Boys	Netter	9.99m	Newlyn
p	PZ1218	Sarah Steve	Angler	8.01m	Penzance
	R	**Ramsgate**			
p	R39	Claire Louise	Potter	8.6m	Brixham
p	R84	Bumble B	Potter	5.9m	Brixham
p	R159	Maret	Netter	12.2m	Looe
	RO	**Rothesay**			
	RR	**Rochester**			
	RU	**Runcorn**			
	RX	**Rye**			
p	Ex RX39	Lisa Ann	De-registered	12.8m	Ex Plymouth
p	Ex RX76	Lumbering Elephant	De-registered	9.9m	Exmouth
p	Ex RX155	Hercules	De-registered	13.9m	Plymouth
p	RX227	Soft Shadow	Netter/Potter	8.5m	Mevagissey
p	RX369	Lisana Ex Bethan Louise	Potter	7.2m	Teignmouth
	RY	**Ramsey**	**(I.O.M)**		
	SA	**Swansea**			
	SC	**Scilly**			
p	SC2	Lowena	Potter	6.7m	Scilly
p	SC3	Coriana	Netter/Potter	7.8m	Hayle
p	Ex SC4	Rockhopper	De-registered	4.7m	Scilly
p	Ex SC8	Samson	De-registered	7.68m	Scilly
p	SC11	Victory of Helford	Netter	10.73m	Scilly

ALPHANUMERICAL INDEX by REGISTRATION NUMBER

p	SC16	Northern Star	Potter/Liner	4.45m	Scilly
p	SC17	Atlantis	Potter/Liner	6.43m	Scilly
p	SC19	Forget-Me-Not	Potter	6.4m	Newlyn
p	SC21	Nazarene	Liner	4.8m	St Ives
p	SC22	Penguin	Potter	7.92m	Scilly
p	SC25	Northwood	Potter	8m	Looe
p	SC27	Isis	Netter	7.62m	Fowey
p	SC32	Vicky Anna	Netter/Potter	9.78m	Scilly
p	SC35	Emerald Dawn	Potter	7.77m	Scilly
p	SC41	Pioneer	Netter/Potter	8.02m	Scilly
p	SC46	Swan Dancer	Trawler	9.75m	Scilly
p	SC50	Boy Jan (Ex Zephyr)	Liner	5.8m	Newlyn
p	Ex SC53	Heather Ann	De-registered	8.1m	Ex Padstow
p	Ex SC60	Leonora	De-registered	6.6m	Mevagissey
	Ex SC64	Tern	De-registered	4.91m	Ex Falmouth
p	SC66	Hustler	Potter	9.8m	Dartmouth
p	Ex SC70	Curlew	De-registered	8.23m	Scilly
p	SC73	Steren-Mor (Ex Pioneer II)	Netter	7.1m	Scilly
	SC76	Pelican		4.46m	Scilly
p	Ex SC77	Ceres	De-registered	8.1m	Ex Looe
p	SC80	Violet May	Potter	5.8m	River Yealm
p	SC84	Faith	Netter/Potter	6.2m	Teignmouth
p	ExSC142	First Swallow	De-registered	<5m	Scilly
p	SC163	Kameruka	Potter	7.4m	Scilly
p	SC164	Emma Rose	Netter	7.47m	Padstow
p	SC167	Maiden Bower	Potter	7.92m	Scilly
p	SC168	Boy Adam	Potter	4.73m	Scilly
p	SC169	Lorraine Ruth	Netter/Potter	8.28m	Scilly
p	SC170	Karenza	Netter/Potter	6.16m	Scilly
	SC171	Marlin		4.4m	Scilly
p	SC172	Pontious	Potter	6.52m	Scilly
p	SC173	Resolution	Netter/Potter	7.95m	Scilly
p	SC175	Marauder	Trawler	9.96m	Scilly
p	SC177	Gallos	Trawler	7.36m	Scilly
	SD	**Sunderland**			
p	SD80	Girl Jane	Trawler	11.6m	Polperro
p	SD201	Neptune	Scalloper	9.95m	River Tamar
p	SD383	Freedom	Trawler	10m	River Tamar
	SE	**Salcombe**			
p	Ex SE1	Summerwine	De-registered	7.13m	Teignmouth
p	SE2	Sea Vixen	Potter	6.9m	Plymouth
p	SE3	Two Boys	Angler	4.0m	Salcombe
p	SE5	Anglo Dawn 11	Angler	9.9m	Salcombe
p	Ex SE8	Emma Jo	De-registered	5.64m	Hope Cove
p	Ex SE9	Girl Jean II	De-registered	8.1m	Ex Hope Cove
p	SE10	Blue Plover	Potter	6.5m	Hayle
p	SE11	Swift	Netter	4.83m	Salcombe
p	SE14	Ann	Liner	7m	Salcombe
p	SE15	Kevi-Tor-Ru	Netter/Potter	6.1m	Salcombe
p	SE18	Charlotte Ann	Potter	5.95m	Salcombe
p	SE20	Little Emiel	Potter	6.2m	Brixham
p	Ex SE21	TT SW Lady	De-registered	5m	Salcombe
	SE21	Sou'West Lady	Potter	11m	Poole
p	SE25	Allicia	Netter/Liner	6.2m	Salcombe
p	Ex SE26	Tarka	De-registered	<6m	Salcombe
p	SE29	Sunseeker II	Netter/Potter	6.9m	Brixham
p	SE33	Phoenix	Potter	9.9m	Salcombe
p	SE34	Pen Glas	Potter	18.4m	Salcombe
p	SE35	Crustacean	Netter	8.2m	Salcombe
p	SE40	Katrina	Scalloper	10.0m	Brixham
	Ex SE44	Iris May	De-registered	8.4m	Milford Haven
p	SE46	Cutsetter	Netter/Liner	6.5m	Salcombe
p	SE58	George Edwin	Netter/Potter	10.5m	Salcombe
	SE70	Chance		5.5m	Ex Hope Cove
	SE71	Tardy	Netter	5.6m	Salcombe
p	SE74	Salcombe Lass	Netter/Potter	11.0m	Salcombe
p	SE75	Galloper	Out of Area	6.3m	Oban
	SE89	New Horizon		5.8m	Ex Hope Cove

p	SE101	Emma Jane	Potter	18.4m	Salcombe
	SE119	Dolly Ann	Potter	11.9m	Weymouth
p	SE122	Guillemot	Netter	6.43m	Salcombe
p	SE138	May Queen	Liner	4.0m	Salcombe
	SE142	Nicks		3.9m	Salcombe
p	SE150	Claire Louise	Trawler/Potter	11.9m	Salcombe
	Ex SE152	Sally	De-registered	5.2m	Salcombe
p	SE154	Bung	Potter	5.0m	Salcombe
p	SE156	Artful Dodger III	Potter	8.2m	Kingsbridge
p	SE158	Martlett	Angler	6.0m	Salcombe
p	SE322	Carpe Diem	Netter	5.9m	Mevagissey
	Ex SE324	Dolphin	De-registered	4.9m	Ex Salcombe
p	SE328	Leo 2	Crabber/Liner	4.9m	Salcombe
p	SE330	Emily Ann	Liner	4.5m	Salcombe
p	SE332	Peadar Elaine	Potter	18.4m	Salcombe
p	SE333	Minstral	Potter	5.5m	Salcombe
p	SE334	Elizabeth	Angler	8.24m	Salcombe
	SE343	Toutai		5m	Salcombe
	SE371	West Wind		4.4m	Dartmouth
	SH	**Scarborough**			
p	Ex SH76	Wayfinder	De-registered	13.2m	Newlyn
p	Ex SH127	Boy Steven	De-registered	8.1m	Padstow
p	SH279	Adella (Ex Jodan C)	Trawler	9.3m	Newlyn
p	Ex SH297	Shanice Patricia (Ex Nirvana BM489)	De-registered	9.96m	Brixham
	SM	**Shoreham**			
p	SM77	Lindy Lou	Potter	4.3m	Clovelly
p	SM241	Two Brothers	Traw/Scallop	11.9m	Exmouth
p	SM271	Angelena	Trawler	13.99m	Exmouth
p	SM690	Sea Gem	Netter	5.1m	Exmouth
p	Ex SM785	Our Diana	De-registered	22.8m	Visitor
p	SM799	Charella of Shoreham	Trawler	11.9m	Looe
	SN	**North Shields**			
	SO	**Sligo**	**(Eire)**		

p	SO958	Eternal Dawn	Pair Trawler	22.75m	Visitor
	SS	**St Ives**			
p	SS1	Cornish Crest	Angler	9.1m	St Ives
p	SS3	Guide Me	Liner	5.7m	Mevagissey
p	SS7	Diana	Liner	4.9m	Sennen
p	SS8	Asper	Netter/Liner	9.2m	St Ives
p	SS11	Charisma	Liner	5.1m	St Ives
p	SS17	Osprey	Netter	5.0m	St Ives
p	Ex SS19	Dino	De-registered	4.4m	Helford R.
p	SS21	Hanna G	Netter/Liner	6.3m	St Ives
p	SS23	Roannah E xYH800	Trawler	9.96m	Newlyn
p	SS25	Kelly Girl	Netter	5.8m	St Ives
p	SS28	Lamorna	Netter	12.om	Newlyn
p	SS32	Sea Breeze	Netter	8.3m	St Ives
p	Ex SS40	Shamrock	De-registered	5.57m	Ex Newquay
p	SS40	Tollbar	Liner	5.8m	Newquay
p	SS45	Shannon	Netter/Potter	9.2m	Newquay
	Ex SS47	May	De-registered	9.3m	Ex St Ives
p	SS50	Early Dawn	Liner	6.3m	St Ives
p	SS52	Aurora	Netter	9.6m	Newlyn
p	SS53	Norah-T	Liner	5.6m	St Ives
p	SS54	Caliope	Liner	4.5m	St Ives
p	Ex SS59	Honey Bee	De-registered	5.7m	Newlyn
p	SS65	Hope	Liner	4.7m	Newlyn
p	SS66	Phra-Nang	Potter	8.3m	Hayle
p	SS67	Tracey Clare	Netter	9.94m	Helford River
	Ex SS70	Teal	De-registered	4.53m	Ex Falmouth
p	SS76	Tillerman	Liner	5.9m	St Ives
p	SS80	Little Christina	Netter	7.5m	St Ives
p	SS85	Merlin	Liner	4.8m	St Ives
p	SS87	Pride of Cornwall	Netter	9.9m	Newlyn
p	SS88	Tegen Mor	Net/Pot/Liner	10.8m	Hayle
p	SS92	Elishia	Netter/Liner	5.6m	Newlyn
	Ex SS94	Three Brothers	De-registered	4.7m	

ALPHANUMERICAL INDEX by REGISTRATION NUMBER

p	SS96	Lady Anne	Liner	5.2m	St Ives
p	SS104	Girl Karen	Netter/Liner	7.8m	St Ives
p	SS112	Jonathan Seagull	Netter	5.2m	St Ives
p	SS118	Crystal Sea	Trawler	21.6m	Newlyn
p	SS126	Nikki Louise	Netter	6.25m	Newlyn
p	SS134	Huers	Netter	11.0m	Newlyn
p	SS136	Cynthia	Liner	5.6m	Newlyn
p	SS138	Peter Pan	Liner	5.7m	St Ives
p	SS142	Carrie-Ann Lady	Crabber	6.2m	Plymouth
p	SS144	Janet Anne	Netter	5.6m	St Ives
p	SS148	My Partner	Netter	9.3m	Falmouth
p	SS149	Maranatha	Potter	5.94m	Scilly
p	SS150	Bethany	Netter/Potter	4.7m	Beer
p	SS151	Hawk	Netter/Liner	5.6m	Mousehole
	Ex SS152	Gwen	De-registered	4.6m	Ex Penzance
p	SS170	Jen	Liner	4.9m	St Ives
p	SS173	Rhiannon Jane	Netter	5.9m	Mevagissey
p	Ex SS189	Boy Darren	De-registered	9.4m	Padstow
p	SS194	Fiona & Tracy	Potter	5.3m	St Ives
p	Ex SS209	Still Waters	De-registered	6.3m	St Ives
p	Ex SS221	Julia Nadine	De-registered	4.3m	St Ives
p	Ex SS224	Mariner	De-registered	5.1m	St Ives
p	SS225	Provider (Ex Minstrel)	Potter	5.6m	St Ives
p	SS226	Daphne Rose	Liner	4.8m	Penberth
p	SS233	Tryphena	Liner	5.6m	Newquay
p	Ex SS242	Ivy	De-registered	5.3m	Newlyn
p	SS252	Wayfarer	Trawler	20m	Newlyn
p	Ex SS258	Nicola Marie	De-registered	5.6m	St Ives
p	SS261	Ammo	Netter	5.4m	St Ives
p	SS262	Anna Maria (Girl)	Potter/Liner	6.5m	Hayle
p	SS266	Belle Bettina	Netter	5.6m	St Ives
p	SS268	Razorbill	Netter	5.6m	Cadgwith
p	Ex SS272	Alison	De-registered	4.8m	Ex Plymouth
p	SS273	Orion	Netter/Liner	8.0m	St Ives
p	SS276	Boy Chris	Liner	4.7m	Newlyn
p	SS284	John Wesley	Trawler	12.0m	Looe

p	SS294	Sea Jay	Netter/Liner	5.6m	St Ives
p	Ex SS295	Kiskey	De-registered		Sennen
p	SS665	Brissons	Liner	4.8m	St Ives
p	Ex SS667	Jae	De-registered	4.8m	Looe
p	Ex SS670	Ray of Hope	De-registered	4.8m	Mousehole
p	Ex SS671	Boy Louis	De-registered	4.8m	Porthleven
p	SS673	Maid Mel	Netter/Liner	5.7m	Hayle
p	SS681	Lady Joan	Liner	5.7m	St Ives
p	SS683	Marlin G	Netter/Liner	5.6m	Hayle
p	SS685	Fou de Bassin	Liner	5.46m	Hayle
	Ex SS686	Jenny Lee	De-registered	8.0m	St Ives
p	SS687	Dillan	Potter	4.9m	Padstow
p	SS689	Ohio	Angler	5.6m	Polperro
	Ex SS692	Jessica Poppy	De-registered	5.9m	Penzance
	SS693	Sea Hawk		4.45m	Sennen
	SS694	Midge		5.55m	Hayle
p	SS695	Keriolet	Netter/Potter	11.4m	Padstow
p	SS697	Elle V	Liner	6.9m	Hayle
p	SS698	Midnight Express	Potter/Liner	9.4m	St Ives
p	SS699	(Ex Boy Dylan)	Out of Area	5.9m	Ex Hayle
p	SS700	Highlander of Hayle	Ring Netter	8.4m	Newlyn
	SS702	Antigri		4.42m	Newlyn
p	SS704	Chloe Estelle	Netter	8.0m	Hayle
p	SS706	Nessie	Netter	8.7m	Hayle
p	SS707	Orca	Netter/Liner	6.9m	Hayle
p	SS710	Sally	Potter	6.11m	Hayle
p	SS711	Bonito	Angler	7.17m	Falmouth
p	SS713	Lyonesse	Liner	5.06m	Hayle
p	SS716	Shikari	Liner	5.68m	St Ives
p	SS717	Boy Daniel	Liner	5.5m	St Ives
p	SS718	Eel-Avum	Netter	5.18m	Penzance
	SSS	**South Shields**			
	ST	**Stockton**			
	SU	**Southampton**			
p	SU511	Kathleen	Trawler	11.9m	Looe
p	SU513	Faith	Trawler	10.0m	Polperro

ALPHANUMERICAL INDEX by REGISTRATION NUMBER

p	SU514	Hope	Trawler	11.99m	Polperro
p	SU515	Charity & Liberty	Trawler	14.95m	Looe
	SY	**Stornoway**			
p	SY5	Ocean Harvest	Trawler	11.4m	Mevagissey
p	SY16	Jacamar II	Trawler	9.66m	Visitor
p	SY36	Lamorna	Potter	9.9m	Padstow
	TH	**Teignmouth**			
	TH7	Amadeus	Out of Area	24.5m	Stornoway
p	Ex TH12	Gipsy Mermaid	Gaff Ketch	11.8m	Plymouth
p	TH19	Henry	Netter	5.5m	Teignmouth
p	TH20	Margaret	Netter	5.5m	Teignmouth
p	TH21	Eyecatcher	Potter	5.7m	Lynmouth
p	TH22	Jodie V	Angler	7m	Seaton
p	TH24	Midnight Sun	Trawler	12m	Plymouth
p	TH37	Alice	Netter/Potter	5.8m	Teignmouth
p	TH52	Grey Dawn	Potter	8.1m	River Tamar
p	Ex TH64	Hopkins I	De-registered	4.9m	Teignmouth
p	Ex TH71	Polarlys	De-registered	5.0m	Teignmouth
p	TH74	Saleda Blanche	Liner	5.7m	Torquay
	TH82	Moira F		4.14m	Teignmouth
	Ex TH84	Robert	De-registered	3.9m	Ex Mevagissey
p	TH86	Sammy B	Netter	4.7m	Teignmouth
p	Ex TH115	Santoy	De-registered	4.88m	ExTeignmouth
p	TH117	Girl Rona	Scallop/Netter	15.1m	Teignmouth
p	TH119	Three Fevers	Potter	6.96m	Teignmouth
p	TH121	Diverse	Potter	5.0m	Teignmouth
p	TH135	Rock Hopper	Potter	4.9m	Paignton
p	TH148	Triton	Angler	7.5m	Newlyn
p	TH155	Deepcore	Netter/Potter	5.7m	Teignmouth
p	TH165	Boy Karl	Netter	5.7m	Teignmouth
p	TH169	Gerry Ann	Trawler	11.7m	Looe
p	TH257	Gerry Ann C	Trawl/Scallop	15.2m	Brixham
p	TH260	Girl Tracey	Potter	5.2m	Torquay
p	TH287	Leonara	Potter	6.0m	Hope Cove
p	TH288	Golden Lancer	Potter	9.9m	Padstow
p	TH417	Valkyrie	Potter	5.6m	Teignmouth
p	TH419	Emaley	Potter	6.0m	Torquay
	TH420	Amanda Jane	Potter xDH66	11.25m	
p	TH422	Silver Fox	Angler	8.09m	Teignmouth
p	TH424	Kay-LarieExWally	NetterxSU414	6.6m	Teignmouth
	TN	**Troon**			
p	TN2	Tobrach-n	Scalloper	23.1m	Visitor
p	TN36	Mattanja	Beam Trawler	32m	Visitor
p	TN37	Philomena	Scalloper	30.6m	Visitor
p	TN38	Georg'Lou N	Scalloper (ExPZ87)	25.5m	Visitor
p	Ex TN39	Piedras	De-registered	35.5m	Visitor
	TO	**Truro**			
p	TO4	Zona	Mussel Dredger	4.3m	Falmouth
	TO9	Iris Elizabeth		7.56m	Ex Falmouth
p	TO40	Intuition	Potter	18.0m	Newlyn
p	TO41	Boy Ryan	Netter	4.8m	St Ives
p	TO46	Shamrock	Netter	5.95m	Padstow
p	TO48	Good Fortune	Potter	7.99m	Portreath
p	TO49	Lower Lights	Potter/Liner	5.6m	Falmouth
p	TO50	Cesca (Ex Accord)	Netter(Ex FR1)	16.46m	Newlyn
	TT	**Tarbert**			
p	TT177	Golden Harvest	Netter	17m	Newlyn
p	Ex TT254	Bain Hope	De-registered	9.65m	Ex Clovelly
	UL	**Ullapool**			
p	UL2	Celestial Dawn	Trawler	11.4m	St Mawes
p	UL4	Star of the North	Netter	8.49m	Scilly
p	UL178	Eclipse	Potter	7.9m	Newquay
	W	**Waterford**	**(Ireland)**		
p	WD87	Molly B	Beam Trawler	35.5m	Visitor
p	WD149	Alicia	Beam Trawler	34.41m	Visitor
p	WD220	Mary Kate	Beam Trawler	24.45	Visitor
	WA	**Whitehaven**			
p	Ex WA254	Dabar	De-registered	9.0m	Fowey
	WH	**Weymouth**			
p	WH26	Charjon	Potter	4.58m	Seaton
p	WH97	Dragun-An-Moar	Netter/Potter	6.6m	St Ives

p	WH111	Bethany J	Potter	8.4m	Padstow
p	WH115	Boa Pescador	Netter	8.1m	Porthleven
p	WH264	Prospector	Potter	9.9m	Newlyn
p	WH454	T K	Potter	6.2m	Bude
p	WH461	Davrik II	Netter	9.8m	Salcombe
p	WH578	Boy Brax (Ex Amro)	Netter/Liner	5.6m	St Ives
p	WH584	Kaluger	Trawler	9.9m	Brixham
p	WH696	EtoiledesOndes	Potter	16.2m	Teignmouth
p	WH707	Zaranathax	Trawler	9.8m	Plymouth
	WI	**Wisbech**			
	WK	**Wick**			
p	WK3	Ben Loyal	Netter	21.2m	Newlyn
p	WK127	Osprey	Netter/Potter	9.9m	Porthleven
p	WK349	Stephanie	Trawler	13.7m	Bideford
p	WK799	Carly Anne	Netter	7.7m	Plymouth
	WN	**Wigtown**			
	WO	**Workington**			
	WY	**Whitby**			
p	WY1	Walrus	Netter	10.9m	Ilfracombe
p	Ex WY36	Ocean Venture2	Now FY367	11.0m	Ex Falmouth
p	WY335	Sardia Louise	Netter	10.9m	Newlyn
p	WY379	Carol H	Trawler	18.7m	Newlyn
p	ExWY788	Christy G	De-registered	9.9m	Salcombe
	YH	**Yarmouth**			
p	YH1	Pioneer	Whelker	9.2m	Bideford
p	Ex YH5	Golden Harvest	De-registered	7.05m	Exmouth
p	YH299	Mary D	Potter	8.5m	Port Isaac
p	YH320	Northern Lights	Potter	9.5m	Newquay

MY BOAT LIST

REG. No.	BOAT NAME	WHERE SEEN	DATE	COMMENT